THE QUESTION OF OFFSHORE OIL

A conference sponsored by the
American Enterprise Institute's
National Energy Project

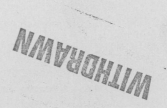

THE AEI
NATIONAL ENERGY PROJECT

The American Enterprise Institute's
National Energy Project was established in early 1974
to examine the broad array of issues
affecting U.S. energy demands and supplies.
The project commissions research into all important
ramifications of the energy problem—economic
and political, domestic and international, private
and public—and presents the results
in studies such as this one.
In addition it sponsors symposia, debates, conferences,
and workshops, some of which are televised.

The project is chaired by Melvin R. Laird,
former congressman, secretary of defense,
and domestic counsellor to the President,
and now senior counsellor of *Reader's Digest*.
The advisory council represents a wide range of
energy-related viewpoints.
Professor Edward J. Mitchell of the
University of Michigan is the project director.

Views expressed are those of the authors
and do not necessarily reflect the views of
either the advisory council and others associated with
the project or of the advisory panels,
staff, officers, and trustees of AEI.

THE QUESTION OF OFFSHORE OIL

Edited by Edward J. Mitchell

With a foreword by Tom Bradley

ISBN 0-8447-2078-X (Paper)
ISBN 0-8447-2079-8 (Cloth)

Library of Congress Catalog Card No. 76-16665

Printed in the United States of America

MAJOR CONTRIBUTORS

Tom Bradley
Mayor, City of Los Angeles

Brendan Byrne
Governor, State of New Jersey

E. J. Cahill
Standard Oil Company of California

Jacques-Yves Cousteau
Chairman, Eurocean and the Cousteau Society

John Devanney
Professor of Marine Systems, Massachusetts Institute of Technology

Robert Dorfman
David A. Wells Professor of Political Economy, Harvard University

Darius Gaskins
Director, Office of Outer Continental Shelf Program Coordination,
Department of the Interior

William Hargis
Dean, School of Marine Science, College of William and Mary, and
Director, Department of Marine Science, University of Virginia

L. P. Haxby
Manager, Environmental Affairs, Shell Oil Company

H. J. Haynes
Chairman of the Board, Standard Oil Company of California

Barbara Heller
Environmental Policy Center

Royston Hughes
Assistant Secretary, Program Development and Budget, Department of the Interior

J. R. Jackson, Jr.
Exxon Corporation

Robert Knecht
Director, Office of Coastal Environment, National Oceanic and
Atmospheric Administration

Charles Matthews
President, National Ocean Industries Association

Walter Mead
Professor of Economics, University of California, Santa Barbara

Leonard Meeker
Center for Law and Social Policy

William Menard
Professor of Geology, Scripps Institution of Oceanography

Edward Mitchell
Director, National Energy Project, American Enterprise Institute, and
Professor of Business Economics, University of Michigan

Richard Perrine
Professor of Engineering, University of California, Los Angeles

William Radlinski
U.S. Geological Survey

Francis Sarguis
President, Get Oil Out, Inc. (GOO)

Carl Savit
Senior Vice President, Western Geophysical Company of America

Robert Solomon
California Energy Conservation Commission

Irvin L. White
Professor of Political Science and Assistant Director, Science and
Public Policy Program, University of Oklahoma

CONTENTS

FOREWORD

The American Enterprise Institute for Public Policy Research, with its Conference on the Costs and Benefits of Offshore Oil Exploitation, has again arranged an especially timely and relevant exchange of ideas. I am pleased to have served as chairman of this second major event held under the auspices of the National Energy Project.

The question of methods of recovery and the appropriate disposition of oil from the outer continental shelf represents an immediate and burning issue within the project's primary objective: to develop a coherent energy statement contributing to national policy. Since the events of the winter of 1973, the nation has come to recognize the need to establish a rational framework through which can be judged individual issues of pressing importance such as offshore oil.

Only in recent months have we begun to grasp the extent of the great shift in understanding the true value of nonrenewable resources and the major adjustments in procedures and institutions that must occur if we are to pursue appropriate policies.

In the charged atmosphere that has accompanied this shift, there is a vital need to develop a clear perception of the elements which will comprise our new assumptions. Such an understanding will be our only safeguard against error when prompt action is so clearly needed.

I am gratified that this cause is being so ably and evenhandedly pursued in the work of the National Energy Project.

June 1975

TOM BRADLEY, *Mayor*
City of Los Angeles

INTRODUCTION

Edward J. Mitchell

On March 20 and 21, 1975, AEI's National Energy Project held its second conference in a series devoted to the nation's major energy policy issues. The subject was
offshore oil: costs versus benefits and the site was Beverly Hills, California. The
issue was and is uppermost in the minds of southern Californians who more than
most have experienced the costs and the benefits of offshore drilling and who should
have an important voice in the debate over future federal policy on offshore drilling.

This issue is dominated by two considerations: economic value and environmental risk. To the economist it is a classic problem involving the tradeoff between
competing social values. The controversy, as readers of these pages will see, is not
so much about the magnitude of the economic value of offshore oil, or even the
probability of environmental mishaps, but about the social value to be placed upon
a clean natural environment and the social loss associated with oil spills and other
environmental damage. On this question the clash between environmentalists and
those favoring accelerated drilling was most pronounced. Indeed, it is fair to say
that some at the conference did not even care to consider the economic benefits,
holding the environment to be invaluable. Unfortunately, it turns out to be impossible to make rational public decisions when some values are taken to be inestimable.
Whether implicitly or explicitly, we presume a value for everything when we make
choices, and it is certainly an aid to good social choices to make our valuations
explicit.

Those presenting papers at the conference were not at all hesitant to tackle
the question of value. Professor Robert Dorfman of Harvard began with the
(relatively) easy job of assessing economic benefits. He was followed by Professor William Menard of the Scripps Institution of Oceanography, who offered a fresh
approach to the valuation of environmental losses. Professor Walter Mead of the
University of California at Santa Barbara then offered a calculus for comparing
the economic benefits and environmental costs and making sound public decisions.
Professor Irvin White of the University of Oklahoma concluded the first day with
an analysis of the proper procedures for resolving the conflicts and getting on with
the job of developing sound programs in this area. Throughout the day the
comments of the distinguished participants sharpened and clarified the issues.

The following morning four leading figures in the offshore oil debate discussed
the pros and cons of drilling and responded to questions from conference partici-

1

pants. The panelists were Governor Brendan Byrne of New Jersey, explorer and author Jacques-Yves Cousteau, H. J. Haynes, chairman of the board of Standard Oil of California, and Royston Hughes, assistant secretary of the interior for program development and budget. Serving as moderator of this discussion was Mayor Tom Bradley of Los Angeles. The discussion was taped for telecast, and two hours of the program have been shown on hundreds of stations throughout the country.

I think the reader will find that the proceedings of the conference contribute to the objective of the National Energy Project: to present competing views on the major energy issues of our day for the purpose of clarifying the choices and achieving a sound national energy policy.

PART ONE

The Value of Offshore Oil

After opening remarks by Los Angeles Mayor Tom Bradley and by Professor Edward Mitchell, director of the National Energy Project, Professor Robert Dorfman began this session by speaking on the value of offshore oil. Warning that the lack of hard facts would necessarily make his analysis highly conjectural, he estimated that the oil and gas in the outer continental shelf was worth about $100 billion and concluded that these resources could make a significant contribution to the nation's fuel supply. The environmental costs of development would be great, he said, but compared to coal and nuclear power, offshore resources would prove relatively clean environmentally. In the discussion that followed, Professor Dorfman contended it would be worth the costs of a few years' delay in the offshore development of non-gulf areas to get "a better fix" on a "dreadfully uncertain" enterprise. Panel members questioned whether there was enough oil and gas off the Atlantic and Pacific coasts to warrant development. And controversy arose over Professor Dorfman's forecast that the current world market price of oil would fall from $11.00 to $7.00 a barrel by 1985.

THE VALUE OF OFFSHORE OIL

Robert Dorfman

To say anything conclusive on the value of offshore oil would require a battery of crystal balls, and all I have is a middle-sized computer without many data to feed into it. All I can do is present some considerations in the hope of giving us something close to a factual basis for our deliberations.

To define the value of offshore oil means in principle to determine how much worse off the United States would be if the offshore oil did not exist or if we chose not to use it. Without the offshore oil we should either have to use less energy, or have to use more of other domestic sources (such as Western coal or shale oil or nuclear power), or have to import more oil, than we would with it. The value of the offshore oil is therefore the difference between the cost of that oil and the cost of the least undesirable combination of those three broad alternatives. My task is to present an appreciation of these costs: to keep the task within bounds, I will devote almost all my effort to the cost of offshore oil, relying on some general principles and the knowledge of those to whom these remarks are directed to supply the costs of the alternatives to offshore development.

To set the stage, let me rehearse some of the developments along the continental shelf. The continental shelf is the part of the ocean bed that lies under 200 meters of water or less. It varies in width from ten miles or so off Florida to several hundred miles off Maine and Massachusetts. There has been extensive drilling in the continental shelf in the Gulf of Mexico, some off the California coast, and none in the Atlantic or in the Gulf of Alaska. All we now know about the existence of oil and gas in these latter areas is what we can infer from seismic soundings and general geological principles.

When a portion of the shelf is to be developed, it is divided into square tracts, each encompassing nine square miles, and the right to develop each tract is auctioned off to the oil company that makes the highest bid. Before the bidding, the oil companies spend a considerable amount of money gathering and analyzing

Some of the figures in this paper have been adjusted to reflect comments made during the conference. These comments, offered by William Radlinski of the United States Geological Survey and J. R. Jackson of Exxon Corporation, have likewise been adjusted.

I am greatly indebted to Ralph Townsend of the Office of the Outer Continental Shelf Program Coordinator, Department of the Interior, for his assistance in obtaining and interpreting data on the cost of offshore operations. The responsibility for the resulting estimates, of course, is entirely mine.

5

geological evidence for the oil and gas potential of each tract in which they may be interested. Unfortunately, the oil companies' studies are proprietary information, and neither the government nor I know what the oil companies have found. We outsiders have to make do with much cheaper and, correspondingly, more superficial information. But even the oil companies do not really know what is down there, as witness the large number of dry holes, each costing $3 million or more. The American Petroleum Institute has estimated that 90 percent of the exploratory wells drilled offshore fail to find commercially useful deposits.

When the tract has been leased, the lessee drills his exploratory wells—three or four or more of them—and with reasonable luck and wisdom finds and delineates a significant oil deposit. He is now ready to develop the field. His first step is to build a platform on which drilling equipment for production wells, wellheads, and other equipment will be mounted. These days, $25 to $40 million will buy a platform in the open sea large enough to take care of two dozen production wells. One such platform is usually enough for a single nine-square-mile tract. The production wells are then drilled from the platform, each extending some 9,000 or 10,000 feet beneath the ocean floor. They are somewhat less expensive than these preceding items. The cost of a fully equipped well can range from less than $1 million (but not much less) to over $3 million, depending on geological circumstances.

I have dwelt on the monetary costs of doing business on the continental shelf because I find them impressive and because it is important to recognize that they are far higher than the costs of comparable operations on land. But I cannot ignore the environmental hazards. The great danger is blowouts, and they can occur whenever drilling is going on. Practically without warning the drill bit can pierce a pocket containing gas and oil under enormous pressure—indeed, that is what the drillers are hoping for. There are elaborate valves and devices for creating back-pressure to control the surge, but in spite of all skill and precaution, these valves and devices do not always work. Indeed, the fact has to be faced that blowouts are part of the cost of drilling, just as crashes are part of the cost of aviation, in spite of everyone's best efforts. Large blowouts, spills, and fires will be rare, but Santa Barbara and experiences on the Gulf Coast remind us that they will occur.

I have not quite finished the catalog of offshore activities. When the oil and gas are flowing up to the platforms, they have to be processed to remove water and other contaminants, and then shipped to shore. Gas is always shipped by pipeline, while oil may be sent by either tanker or pipeline. Oil pipelines appear to be preferable to tankers for platforms within about 100 miles of the point of shore discharge, while for longer distances tankers are more economical. If tankers are used, deepwater moorings and oil storage facilities have to be provided. Environmental hazards are smaller when oil is transported by pipe than when tankers are used.

Finally, the oil comes to the shore. I pass over the need for refineries, since that need is not peculiar to offshore oil. Both onshore oil and imported oil have to be refined, and if the refining is not done in this country, we must pay to have it done somewhere else. The economic and environmental costs of refining should therefore be charged against the use of gasoline, fuel oil, and other petroleum products rather than against the development of the outer continental shelf. But there is one category of onshore cost that is peculiar to exploiting the continental shelf petroleum. I have emphasized the vast amount of activity that takes place in an offshore oil field: the operations of drilling rigs, platforms, tankers, undersea pipe-laying ships, and so on. All this activity requires onshore support: shipyards, machine shops, materials handling, administration, ground transportation, and storage in profusion proportional to the cost of the offshore activity. That means, of course, both employment and mess.

With my brief sketch for background, we can now discuss the value of the offshore oil and gas. Four broad questions have to be considered: (1) How much oil and gas is there? (2) How much is a unit of oil or gas worth? This, as I said at the beginning, is the cost of the least undesirable alternative to extracting that unit. (3) How much does it cost to find the oil and gas, produce it, and deliver it onshore? (4) What noneconomic costs—environmental and other—are entailed? I shall deal with each question in turn. In so doing I shall lead us into the world of conjecture. It is true that I shall often speak affirmatively, but my audience has been warned.

First, then, how much oil and gas is out there? I have already pointed out that, although there is a good deal of circumstantial evidence about the continental shelf, no one really knows the answer for sure. The most authoritative source of information is the U.S. Geological Survey and I shall follow what it says, with the warning that a controversy about its estimates is now raging. The most recent Geological Survey estimates are summarized in Table 1, along with independent estimates by the National Petroleum Council. It should be noted that the two estimates relate to different entities. The data from the National Petroleum Council are estimates of the amounts of crude oil that, in the judgment of the council's experts, will be found by exploratory drilling and other means in the designated regions. The Geological Survey's estimates take account of the technological difficulties and economic costs of extraction which, generally speaking, limit the amount of oil recovered from a field to a third or less of the total amount underground. The National Petroleum Council's estimates can be converted to rough estimates of recoverable oil by dividing them by three.

Using that conversion, the table shows that the Geological Survey's estimates are, on the whole, more optimistic than those of the National Petroleum Council. The estimates for the potential in the Gulf of Alaska are most sharply divergent. There the National Petroleum Council's estimates imply recovery of about 9 billion

7

Table 1
ESTIMATES OF OIL RESOURCES IN THE CONTINENTAL SHELF

| Area | Geological Survey Estimate of Recoverable Resources[a] | | National Petroleum Council Estimate of Oil-in-Place[c] (billion bbl) |
	Billion bbl	Years' supply[b]	
Atlantic	10–20	1.6–3.2	15
Gulf of Mexico	20–40	3.2–6.4	39
Pacific	5–10	0.8–1.6	50
Gulf of Alaska	30–60	4.8–9.6	26
Total	65–130	10.3–20.6	130

[a] Estimates by U.S. Department of the Interior, Geological Survey, published in Council on Environmental Quality, *OCS Oil and Gas,* vol. 2 (Washington, D. C., April 1974), Appendix E, p. 8.

[b] Computed from preceding column. One year's supply equals 6.3 billion bbl.

[c] Estimates by National Petroleum Council, published in Federal Energy Administration, *Project Independence Blueprint, Final Task Force Report, Oil: Possible Levels of Future Production* (Washington, D. C., November 1974), p. II-13.

barrels, which is less than a third of the lower bound of the Geological Survey's range.

In the face of these discrepancies, I have adopted the Geological Survey's estimates as the most authoritative available.[1] According to these estimates there is enough recoverable oil under the oceans to satisfy America's needs at 1973 levels of consumption for between ten and twenty years. The Geological Survey estimates that there is also enough natural gas in the outer continental shelf to supply the country for seventeen to thirty-four years at the 1973 rate of consumption. A realistic way to appreciate these magnitudes may be to imagine that we exploit the oil in the continental shelf over the course of thirty years. According to the lower Geological Survey estimate, that outer continental shelf oil would then supply, on the average, about a third of our annual national needs over that period at a 1973 rate of consumption. Altogether, there is a great deal of oil on the outer continental shelf and a great deal of natural gas.

Our second question is, How much is the oil worth? The answer to that is even more conjectural than the answer to the first question. The last time I looked,

---

[1] After this paper was written, the Geological Survey revised its estimates sharply downward. The new estimates released in May 1975 state that the chances are 95 percent that the total amount of undiscovered recoverable oil in the outer continental shelf is at least 10 billion barrels but no greater than 49 billion barrels. The odds implicit in the earlier estimates have not been published, but the general impression is a 75 percent reduction in the amount of oil expected to be recovered. For the May 1975 estimates, see U.S. Geological Survey, *Geological Estimates of Undiscovered Recoverable Oil and Gas Resources in the United States,* Circular 725 (Washington, D. C., 1975), p. 29.

the free price of crude oil was between $10.50 and $11.50 a barrel, depending on quality and location. There are good reasons, aside from day-to-day gossip, for believing that this price is too high. On the supply side, at $11.00 a barrel it is highly profitable to produce more crude oil than is now being produced, both from the continental shelf—as we shall see below—and from many other sources. On the demand side, at $11.00 a barrel, oil will be priced out of many important markets. To take an important example, about a sixth of the electric power in the country is now generated in oil-fired plants; this market accounts for about a twelfth of the petroleum which the country consumes. At historical prices the cost of generating electricity in oil-fired plants has been about 20 to 25 percent greater than the cost of generating electricity in coal-fired plants and slightly higher than the cost of generating electricity in nuclear power stations. At $11.00 a barrel, the cost of power from oil-fired plants will be about twice as high as the cost from nuclear plants. To be sure, it takes awhile to build nuclear plants and even to switch over to coal burning, but given an incentive of this magnitude, that result is inevitable.

Each segment of the petroleum market has its own way of responding to higher prices, be it by driving lighter cars, by turning down thermostats, by using cardboard packaging instead of plastic, or whatever. In its studies for Project Independence, the Federal Energy Administration has tried to estimate the effects of higher crude oil prices on the use of petroleum and its products in this country. For 1985 it estimates—or, more accurately, conjectures, though the work was done with great care—that at a price of $11.00 a barrel, petroleum consumption would be 25 percent lower than what it would be at historical prices; at $7.00 a barrel, consumption would be 12 percent lower than what would be expected at old-fashioned prices. The federal energy-saving program, much of which will surely be enacted, will induce still further decreases in consumption.

These considerations persuade me that crude oil prices in the neighborhood of $11.00 a barrel cannot long be sustained. How much prices will come down is hard to quantify, and it depends particularly on the prices for competing fuels and the costs of extracting oil in relatively high-cost areas such as Alaska, the North Sea, and, of course, the continental shelf. In more technical language, the equilibrium price of crude oil depends particularly upon its own supply curve and the supply curves of substitute sources of energy. I have contemplated many of the relevant data and, without the benefit of deep analysis, have come out believing that $7.00 to $8.00 a barrel should approximately balance supply and demand during the period that the continental shelf fields are active. Those are the figures that I shall use in my assessment. I may note, for comparison, that the Project Independence study, with the benefit of deep analysis, arrived at a figure of $7.00 a barrel, or a little less, for 1985.

So far we have considered the volume of the resources in the continental shelf and their unit value. Multiplying the two together, we can obtain the aggregate value that that oil would have if it were found, extracted, landed, and ready for refining without delay. If we use the lower limit of the Geological Survey's estimates, this aggregate value comes to $500 billion; if we use the upper limit, it comes to about $1 trillion. To keep matters simple, I have not made much mention so far of natural gas, but the Geological Survey's lower-limit estimate is that there are 400 trillion cubic feet of natural gas in the shelf, which we may estimate to have an aggregate value at least as great as that of the oil. We are therefore talking about resources worth some trillion dollars, using lower-end Geological Survey estimates, when and if extracted and landed.

Now a trillion dollars is a vivid figure but fundamentally meaningless. The oil and gas have not been found, extracted, and landed, and to make them available will require costly endeavors and long delays. Both the costs and the delays detract from the value of the resources that now lie hidden a mile or two under the sea bed. We must now turn to these subtractions.

The delays in obtaining the offshore gas and oil will be substantial. Virtually no offshore gas and oil is now flowing except off Louisiana and East Texas, and it would hardly be possible for new fields to come on line in less than five years. Even when the resources flow, they do not flow all at once. The general expectation is that the continental shelf will be exploited over a period of thirty years or more, and, naturally, resources that will be available in five to thirty years are not as valuable as resources that are available now. Their value has to be discounted.

Evidently, the rate of discount used is important in the evaluation of activities that are going to extend over thirty-five years or more. Conventional business wisdom holds that an investment is not worth undertaking unless it can be expected to earn a return of at least 15 percent on the funds required. I will not quarrel with that as a business principle, but for purposes of social evaluation 15 percent is much too high; for arithmetic reasons, it implies that all consequences that mature after about twenty-five years will be virtually ignored. There is need for a social rate of discount to be used by responsible government officials and their critics in assessing the desirability of investments and the value of resources.

The social rate of discount is a tricky concept and leads to even greater problems of estimation than that of the future price of oil. It is made up of two components. One is a discount for simple futurity, essentially a moral judgment of the relative importance of providing for our current needs and conveniences as against making provision for the needs and convenience of future generations. There is a school of thought, to which I adhere, that holds there should be no discount for simple futurity, on the grounds that our descendants have as good a claim to inherited resources as we have. But that is a minority view, and, besides, our social choices to date indicate that, in practice, we are not that unselfishly solicitous about the welfare of posterity. So, as a compromise, I have adopted a 2 percent discount rate for simple futurity—a figure which means, roughly, that we judge a million dollars worth of oil available now to be about as important socially as one and a half times that amount to be available in twenty years, disregarding any changes in circumstance that may occur in the interim.

The question of changes in the interim is where the second component comes in. There are sure to be some important changes in circumstance over any long run. In particular, in twenty years we should be substantially richer and more adroit technologically than we are at present. In other words, our unsatisfied needs would not be as urgent and we should have more skill and knowledge available for meeting them than we do now. The fact that per capita income has been growing pretty steadily at 25 percent to 30 percent every decade, along with some strong assumptions and simple calculations, indicates an allowance of 4 percent a year for the effects of economic growth and technological progress. Altogether, then, I believe 6 percent would be an appropriate social rate of discount. By this standard, 1,000 barrels of oil available now have the same social importance as 3,200 barrels available in twenty years.

The economic value of offshore oil and gas depends not only on how much there is, but also on how soon it is developed. The more quickly it is developed, the less the resulting flows will have to be discounted, but also the greater will be the costs of exploration and development per barrel of oil or cubic foot of gas. The "accelerated development" program worked out by Project Independence appears to incorporate the best-informed judgment of what can be achieved by a vigorous but not extravagant effort to develop the mineral resources of the outer continental shelf. The estimates derived here are based on that program.

It has, however, been necessary to depart from Project Independence data in several respects. In the first place, the Project Independence production estimates do not extend beyond 1988, although at that time most of the wells developed under the program will still be producing and, indeed, the annual flow of oil and gas from offshore will not yet have begun to taper off. To fill that deficiency at least partially, the estimates used below include the value of oil and gas produced by wells developed under the Project Independence program throughout the lifetimes of those wells. They do not include the value of fuels produced by wells brought in after 1988, though it is highly unlikely that exploration and development will not cease on that date. The effect of omitting development after the period of the Project Independence plan is abated considerably by discounting: the present value of a well developed in 1989 is only about 40 percent of the present value of the same well developed in 1974, and the value of later wells is discounted even more.

The second major departure from Project Independence is in the area of costs. The Project Independence studies took into account all the oil and natural gas resources of the United States and, therefore, did not devote much attention to the peculiar difficulties of offshore operations. The Project Independence cost estimates often diverge substantially, therefore, from those of other sources. The cost estimates used in this study are based on procedures derived in the Department of the

Table 2
SOCIAL ECONOMIC VALUE OF OIL AND GAS IN OCS DEVELOPED ACCORDING TO PROJECT INDEPENDENCE ACCELERATED DEVELOPMENT PROGRAM
($ billions)

	Region				
	South Alaska	Pacific	Gulf of Mexico	Atlantic	Total
Value of resources in place					
Oil and associated gas	16	31	42	14	103
Nonassociated gas	6	3	62	9	80
Total	22	34	104	23	183
Finding and extraction costs					
Oil and associated gas	10	17	15	9	51
Nonassociated gas	2	1	27	7	37
Total	12	18	42	16	88
Net social value					
Oil and associated gas	6	14	27	5	52
Nonassociated gas	4	2	35	2	43
Total	10	16	62	7	95

Note: All estimates should be believed to at most plus or minus five billion. Oil is valued at $8.00 per barrel delivered onshore, gas at $1.50 per thousand cubic feet. Costs are estimated from Project Independence task force reports and from data provided by Department of the Interior. Estimates include costs and returns of all wells drilled in the period 1975-1988, discounted to January 1975 at a social discount rate of 6 percent.

Interior for valuing leases in the Gulf of Mexico fields. The costs have been adjusted by factors that are inevitably inexact, to allow for the more adverse operating conditions in the Atlantic, Pacific, and Gulf of Alaska. It should be emphasized that we have no practical operating experience in the Atlantic or Gulf of Alaska, the closest approximation being experience in the North Sea fields.

A number of additional minor departures from Project Independence estimates were required in order to put the data in the form required by the changes just mentioned, but these departures were not substantial. The resulting estimates are rough, but the underlying data are too uncertain to warrant refined analysis. The results are shown in Table 2.

The bottom line is the payoff. In aggregate the oil and gas in the continental shelves are estimated to be worth nearly $100 billion. Let me interpret this figure in the light of our guiding definition of social value: how much worse off we should be if there were no offshore oil and gas or if we chose not to use it. In those cases we should have to cut back on some activities that use petroleum energy, activities whose social value is measured by what we are willing to pay for the fuel required,

Table 3

ANTICIPATED PHYSICAL DEVELOPMENT OF
OFFSHORE OIL AND GAS, 1975–1988

Region	Oil		Nonassociated Gas	
	Number of wells[a]	Rate of output (thousand bbl per day)	Number of wells	Rate of output (thousand Mcf per day)
South Alaska	3,025	410	400	1,440
Pacific	19,125	750	875	480
Gulf of Mexico	13,325	750	20,475	8,560
Atlantic	3,875	270	3,675	1,780
Total	39,350	2,180	25,425	12,260

[a] Excludes exploratory wells and wells producing before 1974.
Source: Computed from data developed by Project Independence task forces on oil and natural gas.

or we should have to use oil and gas from other sources, foreign and domestic, whose value is measured by their price. On the other hand, we should save all the expenses of developing and exploiting the continental shelves. The net value of these sacrifices, alternative costs, and saved costs is the roughly $100 billion shown.

About half this value arises from oil and half from nonassociated gas. Two-thirds is attributed to the already well-developed Gulf of Mexico oil and gas fields, for three reasons: the reserves in the Gulf of Mexico are great, exceeded only by those estimated for the Gulf of Alaska; production there is already in progress and is readily expandable, so that output from the Gulf of Mexico is not discounted for as many years as output in the other regions; and operating conditions are relatively benign, so that costs per barrel or per thousand cubic feet (Mcf) of gas are lowest in that shelf. The Atlantic and Pacific shelves, about which so much concern has been expressed, contribute less than a quarter of the total value estimated.

The corresponding physical results, which may be easier to grasp, are summarized in Table 3. Nearly 40,000 producing oil wells and 25,000 gas wells are contemplated, along with large numbers of exploratory wells and (of course) dry holes. Offshore oil production during an average year will be at the rate of about 2 million barrels a day, or roughly one-ninth of the 1975 rate of consumption. The Pacific and Gulf of Mexico shelves are the most important sources. The gas wells will produce about 12 million Mcf a day, which is about a fifth of the current rate of consumption.

Altogether, the development of offshore oil and gas is an impressive undertaking that will make a significant contribution to the nation's fuel supply. Perhaps

I should mention one other indication of the scale of the enterprise: the investment cost of exploration, development, and auxiliary facilities—discounted over time, of course—will amount to about $70 billion.

These impressive undertakings will have extensive environmental consequences. I know of no reasonable way to express the extent of damage to the environment in billions of dollars. Some of the environmental effects are economic and can be evaluated in monetary terms, but I find it a dangerous practice to evaluate what you can and mention the rest, because the dollar sum soon stands for the total in everyone's mind, including the author's. To illustrate the dangers of this practice, I may mention one set of estimates that appears to have been carefully prepared. These estimates cover the monetary cost of damage to property, the cost of cleaning up spills, the reduction in the value of fishing catches, and a few small components of monetary cost. The total of expected monetary costs comes to $250 per acre of offshore oil developed in the Gulf of Alaska, $50 per acre in the region off the Pacific Coast states, and so on. On this basis, the monetary damages would amount to about $430 million—$390 million in the Alaskan Gulf and $40 million elsewhere. These costs are virtually negligible in comparison with the billions of dollars at stake, as estimated in Table 2. That does not mean to me that the environmental costs and dangers are negligible, but rather that the great bulk of them escape methods of appraisal limited to the components that can be reduced to dollars-and-cents equivalents.

In point of fact these tens of thousands of wells and associated pipelines, tankers, barges, drilling rigs, supply ships, terminals—all spilling oil and miscellaneous waste, churning up the bottom of the sea, and having occasional accidents, some serious—are going to do a great deal of damage to the environment. Every oil spill is a tragedy, like a serious fire. Experience indicates that at the contemplated scale of development there will be two or three major oil spills a year. They will not be like the Santa Barbara spill for the most part—that was the largest spill yet recorded from a stationary source. But they will be serious enough and, in all likelihood, the Santa Barbara spill will be duplicated more than once.

The hazards to the environment are especially grave in the Gulf of Alaska, where the seismic conditions, currents, and conformation of the land all make it highly possible for a single large spill to contaminate the sole breeding ground of a species of sea mammals or migratory birds—and thereby eliminate the species. Spills and pipelines also threaten the lower forty-eight states. We are becoming increasingly aware of the critical ecological significance of wetlands and marshes. And where, besides wetlands and marshes (and an occasional beach), are those pipelines and oil spills going to come ashore?

That sounds like an alarmist statement, but it is all true. On the other hand, some consequences that the people fear are not likely to occur. The offshore developments will be too far out and too scattered to affront the eye. Experience in the Gulf of Mexico indicates that offshore drilling and production does not harm aquatic life seriously or destroy fisheries. The ocean is vast and even the millions of barrels of oil that will be discharged into it each year will be diluted to harmless concentrations a few thousand yards from the platforms. There is some danger that the ocean currents will concentrate the oil in a few places, such as the Sargasso Sea, but no ill effects have yet been noted nor have adverse trends been documented.

It would take an ecologist rather than an economist to give an adequate description of the environmental pros and cons that have to be considered. I shall not attempt it. I shall, however, remind you of our basic evaluative standard: that the value of the offshore resources is how much better off we are using them than foregoing them. In the environmental context this requires comparing the environmental damages and dangers of exploiting offshore oil and gas with those of the alternatives of either reduced use of energy or increased strip mining, nuclear energy production, and oil imports.

The most merciful expedient, from the environment's point of view, would be to reduce our use of energy. That expedient is certainly going to be employed, but its usefulness is limited in a country where housing design, the layout of urban areas, the transportation system, and the power supply system are all predicated on the liberal availability of petroleum. The next most merciful expedient would be to increase reliance on imports, but that has unacceptable social and political consequences that I need not detail. We are left, then, with greater reliance on coal and on nuclear power, both of which are at least as objectionable environmentally as offshore oil and gas. On the whole, in fact, it appears that offshore resources are comparatively clean environmentally and that environmental considerations should not much affect the results of the purely economic calculations to which the bulk of this paper is devoted.

COMMENTARY AND RESPONSE

Leonard Meeker

To a noneconomist like myself, Professor Dorfman's economic analysis is clear and readily understood. It does suggest some thoughts which I would like to summarize quickly.

Professor Dorfman has assigned a current valuation of $100 billion to the offshore oil and gas in the United States. These reserves are, of course, far smaller than those in the Middle East petroleum-exporting countries, but they are still of great importance, and it is therefore prudent for us to begin considering the nature of a finite possession, rather than exploiting our outer continental shelf at maximum speed and depleting it by the end of this century, which we could easily do. We ought to draw on the resource according to a carefully considered plan.

I think we need a mechanism for periodic determination of our national energy requirements in the years and decades ahead. Then we need to assess and keep under review the prospects for satisfying a substantial part of our energy requirements from non-OCS sources: I am talking about coal, nuclear energy, solar energy, and other nonconventional energy sources. Finally, we ought to decide from time to time if our current requirements are to be met out of OCS oil and gas.

Professor Dorfman has pointed out that neither the government nor the public has much knowledge of what oil and gas there are in the shelf and where they are located. Even the oil companies do not know enough until they have drilled exploratory wells. This lack of knowledge suggests that rational use of offshore oil and gas calls for a separation of exploratory drilling from leasing and production. Such a separation could be accomplished either by having a federal program of exploratory drilling at government expense or else by granting private industry initial leases for exploration only: the government could then make a separate decision, later, on leasing a tract for production after studying the information obtained from exploration.

This kind of an approach could have at least two advantages in dealing with an important national resource, a resource which the Supreme Court just this week decided belongs to the whole nation and not to the individual coastal states. One advantage is that there would be a far greater assurance that the Treasury would receive appropriate monetary return when it sold leases for oil and gas from the public lands comprising the outer continental shelf. Second, and probably more important, if the government had adequate information at the start, the leasing

17

program could be carried out on a basis of good knowledge of what the resources were and what contribution they could properly make to meeting the nation's energy requirements.

I thought one of the most interesting and important things in Professor Dorfman's analysis was his conclusion that a realistic world market price for crude oil would be substantially below the current $11.00 a barrel. As I understand him, he is saying that it is not economically necessary to pay prices at or near the $11.00 figure in order to provide sufficient incentive for the development of other U.S. energy sources to supplement imported oil. This conclusion, I think, casts substantial doubt on the administration's plan to maintain the current high price level of imported oil. To do that, according to Professor Dorfman's analysis, would be unnecessary in economic terms as well as probably inflationary.

Now, Professor Dorfman has been forthright in acknowledging the conjectural element in his quantifying OCS oil and gas reserves and their dollar value. He has also said very clearly that the element of conjecture is, if anything, more pronounced in the attempt to estimate environmental costs of offshore oil and gas development. I believe it is important to try to internalize the environmental costs (most broadly considered) in estimating the value of offshore oil and gas. I think it may be here that Professor Dorfman's work requires supplementation, difficult though that supplementation is bound to be.

Professor Dorfman said that he was speaking as an economist, giving an economic analysis, and that from an ecological point of view more work needs to be done. I think that is true, difficult though it may be to arrive at reliable figures: certainly I would not be prepared to say, as Professor Dorfman said, that the millions of barrels of oil that will be discharged each year into the oceans would be diluted to harmless concentrations a few thousand yards from the platforms.

I think this problem of the environmental impact suggests two or three needs. First of all, there is a need for good baseline studies of outer continental shelf areas to look at the marine biology conditions before oil and gas production. A second way to aid environmental protection would be to require that the best available technology be employed in the production of the OCS oil and gas. The best available equipment by current standards would serve to increase the safety of operations and to avoid both accidental spills and chronic leakage of petroleum in the sea. A third measure would be to improve the regulation of OCS operations and the enforcement of these regulations. All this will require additional regulatory personnel and greater expertise in the government agency or agencies responsible. I think real consideration ought to be given to entrusting these tasks to the Environmental Protection Agency.

An element that I think Professor Dorfman did not sufficiently take into account in assigning a value to the OCS oil and gas is the onshore impact, both economic and social, from OCS operations. The impact does constitute a real cost in the development of oil and gas, and it must be figured into the net value.

18

Certainly steps ought to be taken to avoid as far as possible or at least to mitigate the onshore impact of outer continental shelf development. Here I think the federal government ought to assume a major responsibility. Under the Coastal Zone Management Act, it can finance both the planning and the measures that are required to avoid or mitigate the effects of OCS development.

One final comment in regard to the different coastal zones. Professor Dorfman's analysis makes a striking point that most OCS oil and gas probably lie under the Gulf of Mexico and the Gulf of Alaska. That surely has a bearing on what ought to be done in the near future about Atlantic and Pacific coast development.

William Radlinski

I think Professor Dorfman has completed his assignment quite successfully for the purposes of this conference. After giving us some relevant background and setting forth some caveats, he identifies four pertinent questions and provides us with his answers. He gives us a value for offshore oil of $100 billion. Fortunately for a discussant searching for discussion, his paper includes a number of statements that can be readily challenged. I suspect that, in some cases, he may have inserted them deliberately. I shall take this opportunity to comment on a few of them. Inasmuch as I am representing the U.S. Geological Survey, I should tell you that we do not make policy as to whether or not offshore areas should be developed. We carefully avoid assuming any such posture in order to maintain our credibility in the two areas where we have prime responsibility: resource investment and OCS lease management. My remarks will be confined to these areas.

Professor Dorfman suggested the government does not have the proprietary information possessed by the industry. The fact of the matter is that in the past we have purchased all of the proprietary data needed to get our job done—as a matter of fact, more than 200,000 line miles of seismic data since 1968. An order issued by the secretary of the interior in December 1974 requires all OCS permit holders to provide us with any data they collect within thirty days after we request it. These proprietary data, in addition to those that we collect ourselves, are used in resource evaluations, tract appraisals, and for environmental protection.

Professor Dorfman refers to a "raging controversy" over resource estimates by the Geological Survey. This reference stems from a recently published report by the National Petroleum Council. But a careful reading of the report will show that the largest differences in estimates are for onshore oil and gas. There is general agreement on the estimates of undiscovered recoverable resources offshore. Even so, the controversy stems from a lack of understanding of the processes used in

19

making these estimates. It should be emphasized that resource estimates are in the same category as Professor Dorfman's estimate of $100 billion as the worth of the offshore oil, which he makes after stating that it would require a battery of crystal balls to be conclusive. It takes courage to come up with hard figures in the world of unknowns.

I should also point out that Professor Dorfman's estimates for offshore resources are for areas of water depths of 200 meters. He defined the continental shelf as extending offshore to 200 meters depth so that the estimates do not include the continental shelf and rise, though it is reasonable to assume that significant quantities of petroleum will be recovered on the continental slope. As a matter of fact, two production platforms have been ordered situated in a thousand feet of water in the Gulf of Mexico and in 850 feet of water in the Santa Ynez area off California. We are already working beyond a 200-meter area or about to work beyond it.

Another factor that was not included in determining the final value are the offshore reserves as distinguished from the offshore recoverable resources. The Geological Survey report which Professor Dorfman cited, which used figures issued in April 1974, shows a range of 4.9 to 12.2 billion barrels of oil reserves. These should be added to the 65 or 130 billion barrels used in Professor Dorfman's equation.

Finally, a word about safety and environmental protection. While Professor Dorfman concludes that offshore resource development is comparatively clean environmentally, he points out that every oil spill is a tragedy. I would agree on the assumption that he means every major oil spill. We at the Geological Survey are working hard for even greater reductions in the accident rate. Our records show that during the past five years no spills of over fifty barrels and no fatalities have resulted from drilling blowouts during OCS exploration. Since 1970 there have been no fatalities and only three oil spill incidents greater than fifty barrels related to blowouts on OCS production platforms. Also, there was a 55 percent reduction in minor spills between 1971 and 1974.

I have been most pleased to have this opportunity to participate in this conference, and I commend Professor Dorfman for his thought-provoking presentation. He has given us a good basis for discussion.

Carl Savit

I did not prepare a set of comments on Professor Dorfman's paper, as the previous two speakers apparently did, largely for the reason that, as I am speaking third, it was almost a certainty that anything that I might possibly plan to say would already have been said. I will, however, comment both on the original paper of Dr. Dorfman, which I found to have been quite excellently prepared, and the two preceding comments.

The first thing that occurs to me in reading this kind of predictive analysis and in listening to the predictive remarks of those who commented on the paper is a rather disturbing episode when I was in the sixth grade in a California school. I was naive and innocent, and my sixth grade teacher lectured to us on the subject of resources in our social science class. He read from our social science textbook to the effect that the amount of oil and gas then available would only last us fifteen years and that we would in fact run out of oil and gas in fifteen years. Now, I was in the sixth grade much more than fifteen years ago. In the intervening period, a number of authoritative predictions of resource supply have been made, and it seems to me that in almost every case, no matter when the prediction was made, the prediction was that we would run out in fifteen years. It seems to be a constant in the prediction process.

The lesson, I think, that this sort of thing teaches—one that has been confirmed experimentally by some psychological studies—is that when we comment on something of which we are uncertain, we grossly overestimate the degree of knowledge that we have. We cannot correctly estimate the degree of our own uncertainty, and very possibly most of our overestimation of our knowledge is attributable to the syndrome that says what we do not know does not exist. I simply mention this in connection with both the original paper and the underlying predictions of the amount of recoverable petroleum which are cited in Mr. Meeker's comments on the dire consequences of one or another of the factors involved.

The kinds of questions that become illuminated once we begin to acquire more information may be exemplified by one statement in Professor Dorfman's paper. He says, "There is some danger that the ocean currents will concentrate the oil in a few places, such as the Sargasso Sea." This is a statement with which I would have agreed a week ago, but I read a scientific journal article just a few days ago, written by some Russian scientists, listing the transparency of the ocean in different parts of the world. And it turns out that of all of the places listed by the Russians, the highest degree of transparency was to be found in the Sargasso Sea. In view of the fact that 2.6 million barrels of oil or tons of oil are already reported by the National Academy of Sciences to be dumped into the ocean each year from transportation activities, I think we can say one little bit of knowledge removes this particular concern.

This tends to lead me to the subject of planning. I will not dwell very long on the evils of planning: those evils have been adequately covered in the current issue of *Technology Review,* the Massachusetts Institute of Technology publication. Let me summarize. Planning by and large has been used by governmental agencies, municipal bodies, and others to freeze a decision program. It has generally been used to prevent the governmental body's reacting to the unexpected in a rational

21

fashion. Planning always prejudges a situation before it happens, so that one does not have to think as things come along.

The most successful societies, the most successful organizations, are those which plan only as much as they must in order to make current decisions and leave their future decisions to be adapted to circumstances. I think we have seen this, or its companion case (overplanning producing inefficiency), in many instances. We can look, for example, at the Soviet Union, which carefully plans everything, including their 300-volume current list of prices of everything in the country. Those of us who have spent much time there have seen the effects of very careful planning of everything: nothing works.

The other comment I would make here on planning and prediction relates particularly to predicting the price of oil. We have several different predictions what the price of oil will be in 1985. We are talking about prices of $11.00 or $7.00, but we have not taken into account the single factor which may have the greatest effect on the price of oil. At the present time, the announced policy of the government of Saudi Arabia is to increase their production capability from the present 9 million barrels a day to 22 million barrels a day. The government, through ARAMCO, has doubled the amount of exploration that is being conducted in Saudi Arabia; the amount of exploration is twice as high today as it was a year ago. There is not much doubt in my mind or in the minds of any people who are knowledgeable about the oil industry that Saudi Arabia will, in fact, be able to produce 22 million barrels a day by 1985. But with 22 million barrels a day available under the control of one single entity, that entity can make the price of oil worldwide go from $1.00 to $20.00, simply by turning a valve one way or the other. Trying to predict what will happen unless we can read the minds of the people who will be in control of that particular valve in 1985 is really whistling in the dark.

If I have sounded too pessimistic here, perhaps it is because as a scientist, and an industrial scientist at that, I have seen, after careful analysis at the beginning, too many plans go too far wrong too often to be at all confident that the best-laid plans will not continue to go wrong.

Robert Dorfman

First, I want to thank the discussants for their contribution, and particularly for being much more kind to me than I deserve. I appreciate Dr. Radlinski's clarification of my remarks about the state of knowledge and ignorance at the U.S. Geological Survey: he has corrected some misapprehensions that I may have given vent to. I guess there is one place in particular where I would want to hold my ground for what is to come. I would insist that there is indeed a controversy raging about the estimates, that the controversy does not relate exclusively to onshore oil, nor does it exclusively come from the National Academy of Sciences study. King Hubbert certainly would not accept the current official estimates. The National Petroleum Council estimates do diverge. I mentioned this situation really as a forewarning of Mr. Savit's points that we cannot even believe the highly respected United States Geological Survey.

I want to thank Mr. Meeker. I stayed carefully away from drawing any policy conclusions on the grounds that, for my purposes, a firm distinction should be made between fact and opinion—or, more accurately, as between opinion as to the facts and opinion as to what should be done. I certainly agree with Mr. Meeker that it would be highly desirable for there to be public exploration by some outside organization before leases are granted for the extraction of oil, for the reasons he gave and for a number of others. The work I did suggests to me, as his work suggested to him, that there may be no great urgency about plunging ahead in the Atlantic and the Pacific continental shelves—perhaps not ever in the Alaskan with its peculiar dangers—because so much of our reliance will in fact be upon the Gulf of Mexico, where we know already pretty much what we are about.

Along with Mr. Savit, I hope I show that I am wary about believing predictions and rigid policies dependent upon them. I do want to point out (as Mr. Savit pointed out with his mention of psychology, which I thought was very perceptive) that we do tend to underestimate our ignorance. That includes underestimating our ignorance of environmental effects: effects we have not now observed or documented may be there and may, indeed, eventually be revealed. Ignorance is neither a ground for alarm nor a ground for complacency. It makes life difficult on both sides.

My last point—relating to Mr. Savit's last point—is that the Saudis may well be able to increase their daily output to twenty-odd million barrels a day or even beyond. If so, they will have the power to drive the price of oil very far down—perhaps to a dollar a barrel, because their extraction costs are only fifteen or twenty cents a barrel—but then having that much productive capacity does not make it possible for them to drive the price up, because, on Mr. Savit's own showing, there is a great deal of oil elsewhere—very likely right under our feet there is a deposit worth extracting at some finite price. Monopolies have it in their power to decrease the price by flooding the market, but so long as there are lots of other entrants, they cannot increase it.

DISCUSSION

PROFESSOR MITCHELL: I will now open the meeting to questions from anyone who cares to comment or make points. I request only that each speaker identify himself for the purpose of keeping a record of these proceedings.

MR. JACKSON: With respect to Mr. Meeker's comment about the revenue split from offshore oil and gas, I would like to put on record the fact that through 1973 the total revenue from offshore production had exceeded something on the order of $15 billion, of which 80 percent had gone to the federal government and 20 percent had gone to the industry. These are published numbers from the United States Geological Survey each year.

DR. GASKINS: I would like to raise two points. First, I was a little surprised when Professor Dorfman seemed to back away from his framework, in which he presented developing the outer continental shelf as an alternative to what would happen if we did not. In particular, I was surprised when he seemed to support Mr. Meeker's view that there was no reason for us to "plunge ahead" in OCS development. The point I would like to make is that there is a cost in delay, and the cost comes in what we do in the meantime. My proposition is that every barrel of oil from the outer continental shelf that we produce over the next five to ten years, whenever we produce it, will displace an imported barrel of oil. If we delay production for a year, it costs us (as a society) something for that delay, because (as a society) we would rather have our real resources now than later. I believe most oil from the outer continental shelf can be produced for less than $5.00 a barrel, with any course of events that is reasonable for the next six or seven years. If the world price of oil remains above $7.00 a barrel, then these oil wells are extremely valuable, and we would like to get the premium as soon as possible, because of the nature of other alternatives.

The second point I would like to make is in response to Mr. Meeker's statement on the $7.00 equilibrium price. I agree with Mr. Savit that it is a very difficult business to forecast equilibrium prices. I know that many reputable economists from Cambridge, Massachusetts—colleagues of Professor Dorfman— have been saying that the cartel would not last. It would seem that it is more durable than some people have thought, and I would point out that there is certainly an outside chance that the cartel will in fact endure longer than we think now. The members of the cartel seem to have demonstrated quite a willingness to cut back their own production as world demand subsides or as production grows elsewhere.

Let us assume that the equilibrium price of $7.00 lasts over the next ten years. Mr. Meeker said that he sees no point in charging ourselves the current high price, if in fact the price in the future will be $7.00. I think he does not understand the basic economic principle here, the principle that if it costs us $11.00 as a nation for the marginal barrel of oil, everyone who contemplates using oil at this time should face that price, and especially the principle that if they do not face that price, we use oil in a wrong way. Likewise, of course, if it costs us at the margin $1.75 for natural gas, every potential user of natural gas should face the same price, otherwise we will be using resources in an inefficient way.

Without defending the administration's plan for breaking the cartel, since the average price in the United States for oil is around $9.00, and since the marginal price for the nation as a whole is $11.00, I would say that there is a good case for raising the current price to the marginal price.

PROFESSOR MITCHELL: Professor Dorfman, would you care to respond? I am also particularly interested in whether your belief that the long-run price will be $7.00 means you believe we should price oil at $7.00 at this time.

PROFESSOR DORFMAN: On that I should agree with Dr. Gaskins. I think where I would disagree is on the implication of this for immediate development on the Atlantic and Pacific coasts. There is much in what he said that delay would indeed be costly, but it would also be advantageous in those cases because what it buys us is information. We are going ahead into some uncertainties that I do not feel in the least complacent about. Before taking irretrievable steps, it seems to me, rather subjectively, that it is worth the price of some small number of years' delay for us to have a better fix on what we are doing.

I would like also, if I may, to respond to the harsh words, and maybe deservedly harsh, that were said about the numbers that I put before you on the basis of Table 3. It may be that a more appropriate answer to those remarks could come from Dr. Radlinski. In any event, my estimates of the number of wells are derived chiefly from the Geological Survey's estimates of how much oil and gas is to be found in the outer continental shelf and what development would be required in order to extract it. Those were the bases of the estimates, and the softest point in them is indeed the underlying notion as to how much oil and gas will be extracted in those regions.

DR. GASKINS: If there are no more major points, I would like to make some small comments. I notice that we all talk about the uncertainty of offshore oil and

26

I think it is wise to remember that when we talk about the desirability of going into one area or another, we are talking about a decision reminiscent of R & D strategies. It would be wise for us, as a nation, not to put all our eggs in one basket. When we look at these estimates for any one area, we should remember that. We have had some great disappointments in our OCS leasing programs. We sold some land off Washington and Oregon in the 1960s, and in fact it did not produce a single barrel of oil or cubic foot of gas.

Along those lines, it is important that if one were going to express the expected value in probability terms, not in point estimates, most likely the specific values would be much higher. My layman's interpretation of the geologic implications in this case is that Southern California is very likely to have oil and gas, whereas Alaska is much more of a wildcat province. A refinement of these figures conceivably would be based on the odds that we face at a given time as to whether those regions are expected to produce oil and gas.

MS. HELLER: I would like to go back to the question how quickly we should develop the continental shelf, given the current price of oil. One thing I have not seen mentioned anywhere is the prospect for getting oil from enhanced recovery or from unitizing existing fields. These seem to me factors in our deciding how quickly we should develop new areas. The National Petroleum Council estimated a few years ago that by 1985 we could be getting more than 40 percent of our oil in the lower forty-eight states from enhanced recovery—secondary and tertiary recovery. It would seem to me that the present price of oil would justify this. Do these considerations fit in anywhere in the Interior Department's rate program?

DR. GASKINS: They went into the calculations of Project Independence, and there are currently some studies going on that would indicate that there is substantial oil that may be recovered through secondary and tertiary projects.

The best estimates that were available in November went into Project Independence, where the results, as you know, show a substantial shortfall in imports without OCS development. It is widely believed that many tertiary projects are not economic at $5.25, and since tertiary recovery projects are applied to fields that are in decline under the current regulations the correct economic incentives are not there. There is one way to cure this that I know, and that would be deregulation of all oil. In that event, all producers and all consumers would seek the same price: I think that we would then have more production or more investment in these secondary and tertiary projects.

MS. HELLER: Could I ask a quick question to follow upon that? If those price incentives were changed, would that change the Interior Department's schedule for leasing?

DR. GASKINS: That question puts me in an awkward position. In fact, we do not have a schedule for leasing: we have a planning schedule that enables us to assess whether we want to lease in any given area. We have had so many setbacks in the past year—the sales seem to get further and further away—that it would take a lot of secondary and tertiary projects for us to wake up suddenly and say, "Gee, we're envisioning driving down the domestic price of oil by our lavish development of the outer continental shelf." We are certainly quite a way from that; but if we had substantial new investment and success in secondary and tertiary projects, it would have an effect on what we anticipate future prices to be, on the value of the OCS areas, and, perhaps, on the appropriate rate of leasing.

MR. CAHILL: I would like to respond to a couple of points, if I may.

On this business of secondary and tertiary recovery, one of the points that is often missed is the extremely rapid decline of existing reserves under the current situation, where we are producing effectively at capacity. The secondary and tertiary recovery will in fact add reserves and will add productive capacity, but with the current decline curve, reserves are not going to last very long in any case.

Dr. Gaskins's appraisal, and I think this is also suggested by most of the reputable forecasts, is that even with OCS development, even with a strong conservation effort, even with continuation of the moderately high prices we now have for energy, imports will still be required throughout the period till 1985 at least.

If I may, I would like to pick up two other very quick points. One of them is that in most of the dialogues on this subject, I do not detect a sense of urgency about the intervening time period between now, the very short term, and some point in the very distant future. We are now importing roughly 35 to 40 percent of our oil. This percentage is going to increase despite conservation, unless we get cracking on the development, not only on offshore oil, but also of other indigenous resources. It will take a long time to implement conservation techniques that amount to anything. It will take a long time to develop OCS oil and develop coal and so on.

The second point concerns Mr. Meeker's comment on the possibility that the government would do the exploration. I think that the availability of knowledge to the government was adequately covered by Mr. Radlinski. I would only point out that under the current lease bonus bidding system, where each company tends to bid on its most optimistic and most competitive appraisal of the value of a property, it is inevitable that the government comes out best. The sum of the bids awarded is the sum of the most optimistic appraisals.

MR. MEEKER: I would like to put a question to Professor Dorfman in the hope of getting us nearer to resolving the matter of prices. The question really arises out of some of Mr. Gaskins's comments.

Professor Dorfman gave a range of $7.00 to $8.00 as an economic price—a marketplace price—for oil in the years ahead, which I take to be a reasonable estimate. I am wondering to what extent that estimate is based on a quantification of the costs of producing oil in the United States (onshore and offshore), and to what extent it is related to the cost of imported oil and would therefore get us into the uncertain area of what imported oil may be going to cost in the future.

In other words, I understood Professor Dorfman to say that we should be evaluating OCS oil according to what it costs us to do without it, and I interpreted the $7.00 to $8.00 figure as what we could expect to buy oil for from some source. I am wondering about the weighting of the cost figures—how much of that $7.00 to $8.00 is based on the costs of imported oil and how much is based on domestic?

PROFESSOR DORFMAN: I find it hard to make the distinction that is asked for. There is really one world oil market and it is hard to decouple domestic and foreign oil costs—indeed, beyond that, to a large extent there is only one energy market. My estimate was heavily influenced by the cost of a Btu from other sources, particularly from coal, where very large expansion is economically feasible at the Btu price corresponding to $7.00 or $8.00 oil. But, also, I was mindful of what Mr. Savit's comments have reinforced, how much oil there is available for prices down to $7.00 and even below, not only in the Middle East but all over. The current high price of oil is accompanied by repeated newspaper reports of new finds, some of which, probably, have actually occurred. The cartel is already facing difficulties in allocating its current production because its potential rate of output is far greater than the world is willing to take off its hands.

PROFESSOR MITCHELL: I think at this point we are going to have to turn to the second panel. The questions that some of you have not yet been able to ask will still be appropriate later on in the day.

PART
TWO

Environmental and Onshore Impact of Offshore Drilling

Professor William Menard opened this session, pointing out that constant changes in marine biology and ocean currents rapidly make environmental assessments of offshore areas out of date. He introduced the idea of measuring environmental impact not in absolute terms but according to the actual exposure of people to environmental "insults." Professor William Hargis suggested that the main environmental effects from offshore drilling would occur onshore as a result of the need for supporting services and facilities. In the ensuing commentary and discussion, the participants were sharply divided over the seriousness of the environmental damage from drilling. They also disagreed over the value of oceanic baseline studies as a means of predicting environmental damage and over how much environmental knowledge should be secured before drilling decisions were made. A dispute also broke out as to whether the federal government knows as much about the quantity of offshore oil as do the oil companies.

THE ENVIRONMENTAL IMPACT OF OFFSHORE DRILLING

William Menard

When, as an oceanographer, I consider the thousands of pages of environmental impact statements for offshore drilling that have been prepared during the last few years, I find myself impressed at the effectiveness of the law as a fund raiser for the environmental sciences. More is known about the environment and environmental impact of offshore drilling than anyone suspected, even though it is not enough. We know that the impact varies with the chemistry and age of the oil—that is, how long it has been exposed to the air and water. We know the impact varies with the species, with the stage of development of the individual organism, and the stage of development of the ecological niche that the oil encounters. We know it varies with the marine sediment. We know the impact varies with the ocean current, with sunlight, and with climate. We know it persists much longer in places where the water freezes over the winter.

That what is known is not enough will be clearly demonstrated by the fact that this paper will be followed by discussions of a formal type in which divergent viewpoints are represented. I could attempt here to sift and distill the thousands of pages to provide a summary of environmental impact data but this has been done again and again. In the time available to us this morning, I do not think that I could read even the titles of all the papers that have been written about the environmental impact of oil. While none of us can be familiar with all that is known, what is known exists for all of us to read when the need arises. Instead of providing a summary, I shall attempt to focus attention on what I consider to be the valid reasons that divergent viewpoints exist and will continue to exist. I would hope to limit future controversy by stipulating some things that are known or knowable and some things that are inherently unknowable in the time span we are considering. Finally, I shall try to show that some of our difficulties in reaching a consensus may derive from our using the wrong measure of environmental impact.

Let me emphasize one point here—a point Mr. Savit touched on. Since we are capable of learning some things about the environment, but not others, within the time span we are dealing with, we may deceive ourselves by thinking we know things when we do not. I am going to look at the significance of the estimates of quantities of oil in the ground, something we have already heard a good deal about. I am going to discuss the significance of variations in nature and how they influence our understanding of the environmental effects of offshore oil. I also want

33

to talk about the standards according to which we rank offshore regions by the environmental impact of oil development. In short, I am speaking on things about which very little is known. I may go far astray, and for this I apologize in advance.

In order to evaluate the probable regional environmental impact of offshore drilling before drilling takes place, it is necessary to know (1) the nature of the environment at present, (2) the natural variations that will occur during the period of the drilling, (3) the intensity and duration of the environmental insults that will be offered, (4) the immediate response of the environment to the insults, and (5) the long-term response of the environment to the insults. So many of these things involve predictions that it is little wonder there is no consensus on the environmental impact of offshore drilling. Still, I believe it is reasonable to expect agreement on the first point. There are few areas where the environment—geology, biology, meteorology and oceanography—are known to the satisfaction of scientists, such as myself, who have special interests to pursue. Probably we never will be satisfied. However, much is known on a regional basis, and special supplementary surveys of all aspects of the environment are required before leasing takes place.

We could carry out a detailed survey of the existing environment off southern California or any other region: I would think, being myself in the oceanographic business, that we ought to be able to make such a survey in two years or so. Perhaps it could be stipulated that no more than two years of environmental surveying should be required in a region after the first intention to consider leasing is published. The surveying would have to be adequately supported to satisfy the specialists, but it would have a definite end—except, of course, for detailed surveys of the proposed sites for platforms and pipelines. But we would never know everything I want to know about the marine geology off southern California—indeed, if we did, I would be out of business. Experts will always want more information, and properly so. Certainly in a reasonable length of time, we could find out what is there—but what would it mean to know what is there? One of my most distinguished colleagues in marine geology absolutely refuses to have any association with baseline studies, on the grounds that they are totally meaningless.

Although the geology does not change rapidly, the biology and the currents change. If we measure something now, we still do not have any idea what it will be like next year. It surely will not be like what it is, nor, emphatically, will the environment remain constant for the next several decades—which is the period we have in mind for developing offshore oil. We know that there are major fluctuations in ocean currents and water temperatures over periods of about ten years. We do not know enough to predict them, and there is no real possibility we will know enough to predict them until we have observed at least five periods of fluctuation, about fifty years. A few more years of observations will not tell how the ocean environment will develop in the next few decades. It would be just as reasonable to say that we should not drill for fifty years as that we should not drill

34

for a few years, because there are long-term fluctuations that are as important as short-term fluctuations. Moreover, I suspect, fifty years from now, when we have learned more, we will say there are twenty-year fluctuations that are very important, or fifty-year fluctuations. To describe a static environment will not tell us what impact will be suffered by the environment from offshore oil development (or anything else) in the next fifty years.

There are enlightening examples of biological fluctuations in this very region. It is thirty years now since the famous sardine industry of California collapsed— the one that was featured in *Cannery Row,* the one we all read about. The fishermen were blamed for overfishing, because, of course, someone has to be blamed when nature does something by itself. The University of California began a study on what happened to the sardines. That study has been going on for the last twenty years, and by now the ocean off southern California must be the best studied in the world. It turned out we could not tell anything from studying the currents, but cores of sediment were taken from the ocean basins there in which fish scales were preserved, and the fish scales and sediments therein were dated. What was found was that although there was a sardine population that was being fished up to 1945, in most of the last several centuries, there was not. The sardine, in short, is not a normal resident off the California coast.

Now let us consider what would have happened if continental shelf drilling had just begun off southern California when the sardines suddenly vanished. Something like that is very likely to happen, with just as much real connection with drilling as the collapse of Cannery Row had with overfishing. What I am saying, in essence, is that there are long-term oceanic variations. There is little possibility of informed agreement on the environmental significance of the natural variations that will occur during the development of the continental shelf. Indeed the danger exists that policy makers will believe a few years of measuring ocean currents or other environmental variables is a reasonable compromise between knowing nothing and knowing enough to proceed. This is incorrect. It could be argued that we should therefore not go ahead because we do not know what will happen, or it could be argued that we should therefore go ahead because there is no possibility of knowing what will happen in the time available to us for study. In any case, this variability exists, and it must somehow enter into our calculations.

One of my colleagues, a diver of the highest professional level, recently told me that there is at this instant a ravening pack of about a thousand young sea otters stuck north of Point Conception, off the California coast. He said that when he was a boy in La Jolla, he used to walk along the shores, and there were abalone all over the rocks, but now they have gone—presumably (he thought) because too many boys walked along the beach and there were too many fishermen. Thinking about this one day, he realized that if the sea otters had been in that region, probably there would not have been any abalone at all, because sea otters eat abalone. It may be that the only reason he saw the abalone as a boy was that the sea otters were killed off in the fur hunts earlier on. And when the sea otters come down again, the preserve we are putting off La Jolla is very apt to be raided by them. Sea otters also have effects on sea urchins. Sea urchins damage kelp. Various organisms, including man as well as sea otters, kill the sea urchins. It is a complicated situation, and the balance fluctuates over long periods.

Nevertheless, although the effects of many important environmental variables will not be known for decades or centuries, it may be possible to reach a useful consensus concerning them, the consensus being that there is little point in seeking to delay drilling in order to study environmental variability unless the delay is for decades. Studies of variability should continue during the lifetime of the fields and the operation of the fields should be subject to the same controls that would have been established had a newly discovered dangerous variation been known before leasing.

My third point is concerned with the intensity and duration of insults that will be offered to the environment as a consequence of offshore drilling and related activities. On one aspect there should be agreement. All past experience shows that with present laws and technology there will be some spills, blowouts, and other environmental insults through the three or four decades of drilling and extraction: improvements in equipment and procedures may lower the risk but in any such gigantic enterprise risk cannot be eliminated. What cannot be stipulated is the number or frequency of insults, inasmuch as they depend on the amount of oil and gas, and that amount is not only unpredicted but apparently almost unpredictable.

It has been mentioned that the greatest difference in the estimates that now exist is in how much undiscovered oil remains in the ground in the forty-eight contiguous states, a land area that has been explored in more detail than any other land area in the world over a period of a century. But the range of the estimates was not mentioned. The National Academy of Sciences has recently produced estimates based on privileged information provided by oil companies and the individual work of King Hubbert, who has worked for both the U.S. Geological Survey and the Shell Oil Company, and these substantially agree with the Mobil Oil Company estimates that within the forty-eight contiguous states there are about 13 billion barrels of discoverable and recoverable oil. In passing, I should say that I have spent much of the last year trying to unravel these inconsistent estimates and my own conclusions confirm those of Mobil Oil Company for the land area. The U.S. Geological Survey is the federal agency responsible for estimating oil reserves. It believes that there are 110 to 220 billion barrels of recoverable oil as yet undiscovered in the land area of the forty-eight contiguous states.

That is a very large range for the best known area we have. I think the only conclusion that can be drawn by someone not in the business is that we are not very good at estimating how much oil is in the ground. We drill it, we find it, and apparently that must be that. Either the Geological Survey is way out in left field, or everyone else is way out in some other field. Someone is wrong by an order of magnitude, and it is hard to see how that can be. The policy makers have no way of knowing who is right, and naturally enough they trust the federal agency responsible for making the estimates.

Let us look at the problem of offshore development. Of course, if we do not know how much oil there is where we have been drilling for a century, we surely will not know how much oil there is where we have not been drilling, but for the moment we will let that pass. The estimate by the Geological Survey for the region off southern California is for 1 to 2 billion barrels of discoverable and recoverable oil. The estimates of the Western Oil and Gas Association for discoverable and recoverable oil there range between 6 and 19 billion barrels. The problem is evident. If the Geological Survey is entirely correct for the oil in both places, there is 100 to 200 times as much oil within the dry United States as there is off southern California. However, if the Western Oil and Gas Association is correct, and if Mobil Oil and the National Academy of Sciences (and I will add myself to this distinguished company) are correct, there is just as much oil off southern California as there is in all the forty-eight states. If the federal agency is correct, there might be little point in accepting even a quite minor environmental risk from offshore drilling. If the oil industry is right, a much greater risk might be wholly acceptable because of national shortages and need.

To my mind the offshore estimates are an enigma. In any event the uncertainties are more than sufficient cause for the existence of different viewpoints on whether drilling should be permitted and, if so, on what schedule. There is another question connected with the amount of oil offshore, and that is what the immediate environmental effect will be. In looking at this question, I am sticking with southern California, because I happen to have an office that looks out over the very area that would be drilled. What would be the effect of all that oil? How can we estimate the effect if we do not know how much oil is out there? The Bureau of Land Management of the Department of the Interior has taken a conservative approach in this. It has said, "We will take the largest estimate anyone has given, even though we don't know they are right, and we will calculate what the environmental impact would be if you found all that much oil." This is a step in the right direction, but it is not likely to lead to a consensus on this issue to the extent that the consensus will influence policy. It would be much better if we had some way of finding out how much oil is there before we make the policy decision whether we should go ahead. Since it is obvious enough that a hundred years of drilling on land has not told us how much oil there is onshore, we may ask if it is conceivable that we can find out how much oil there is offshore.

Things are not quite as bad as that question would suggest. Half the oil discovered is found in giant oil fields. After drilling only three wells, for example, the oil companies assured us there were 10 billion barrels of oil available in the Prudhoe Bay area. So, for giant oil fields, one can sometimes estimate quickly how much there is in the ground. It is possible to drill to find out how much there is:

it is possible, that is, to carry out exploratory drilling before making an ultimate decision, and indeed the social arguments are for doing just that. The point is not that the Geological Survey does not know and that the oil companies do know, but that no one knows. Otherwise, we would not have an investment of $600 million by the oil companies to drill off Florida in a place where the holes are dry. No one knows what oil is there for sure until he drills.

I see no way to obtain the information that is necessary for an informed consensus if the existing system of exploration and leasing of the continental shelf continues. At present we have secret exploration, bonus bidding, and standard royalties. The major policy decisions to proceed or not are made in almost complete ignorance. If we were to substitute a system of public exploration followed by bidding with variable royalties, the information necessary for decisions would be on hand before the decisions are made. The government, public, and industry would have some basis for assessing whether and when it is reasonable to go ahead. As an aside, let me state that by "public exploration" I mean exploration the results of which are public knowledge, not exploration by government agencies, except to the extent necessary for management purposes.

My fourth and fifth questions are concerned with the immediate and long-term responses of the environment to the spills and drips that will occur. It seems to me, as a non-biologist, that our knowledge of these complex subjects is in considerable disarray. The best scientists in the field often disagree about the meaning and significance of their results. It appears that the different components of crude and refined oil produce different effects on various organisms according to the climate and other environmental variables. It also appears that the effects of all but the most intense and confined spills disappear within a few years. Likewise, low-level pollution by natural oil seeps off southern California apparently has had little effect on the nearby beaches, and the traumas of oil spills off Louisiana are bearable by a prolific fauna and flora nurtured and toughened by the variable salinity and currents of a great delta. So it appears, at least, but there is no real agreement among the experts, and it may reasonably be asked how there can be any basis for a consensus among the rest of us.

As it is with the physical environment, I believe that it may be useful to reach agreement on the time scale involved in controversy. The proposed offshore development would be finished long before the environment could reach any equilibrium with the pollution. We are talking about a transient phenomenon that might not have permanent biological effects but that might well build up over decades and do such things as introduce carcinogens in the food chain. It will take decades to learn. Thus it might be agreed that a proposal to delay drilling for this cause would be a proposal to delay for decades. It might also be agreed that a proposal to proceed in ignorance of these matters would be a proposal that should be subject to periodic review as we become less ignorant.

38

I would like to touch on the set of standards according to which we rank offshore regions. The Council on Environmental Quality (CEQ) recently ranked regions by how apt they are to suffer environmental damage from offshore drilling. Drilling in the Gulf of Alaska was considered the most hazardous and, therefore, the least desirable. There are earthquakes in profusion, storms, and so on in that gulf. Various regions off the East Coast were judged more desirable for drilling—deserving higher priority. I think the Georges Bank was given the highest priority for drilling, as drilling there was deemed to have the least effect on anything.

Professor Dorfman and I were members of a committee that attempted to help the CEQ in this evaluation, and we agreed that, considering the criteria we were using, the listing was very reasonable indeed. But I have recently come to think that there are different ways of ordering environmental impact, and I would like to suggest one of them here.

Consider the measurement of a rather simple phenomenon—noise pollution. The intensity of noise pollution is not measured in the absolute but with reference to the normal background noise in the circumstances. However, sound engineers must also take into account how people individually perceive noise. A deaf man might not be bothered by jet planes. If we put a runway flight path over a home for the deaf, that does not matter as much as if we put it over a school. If it is a runway that, because of certain wind conditions, is never used in school hours, then it does not matter very much if we put the flight path over a school. The engineers give consideration to the time of day, the frequency of noises, the distance to the listener and so on. If the noise occurs frequently, it is more important than if it occurs infrequently, because people do not suffer as much or feel as strong a trauma from infrequent noise. The end result is a noise exposure forecast (NEF) which is used to identify compatible land use.

Something similar is needed to decide what sites are suitable for offshore drilling. Our present system of selecting sites borders on the chaotic, and it may be because we have attempted to make absolute measurements of environmental impact. Let me propose a perceived environmental exposure forecast (PEEF) with the following formula:

$$PEEF = k \frac{Q F V}{d^2 t}$$

where Q is the quantity of some type of pollution—chemical, visual, audible—F is the number of people close enough to perceive the pollution, d is the distance between the people and the site of the pollution, t is the time between episodes of pollution, V is the velocity at which the pollution propagates, and k is some constant of proportionality. The formula is based on the assumption that wherever there are people there is an environment that provides both pleasure and employment. Accordingly, the more people who are in range to be exposed to an episode of pollution, the greater the perceived environmental exposure forecast. Inasmuch as the pollution can spread in all directions, the perceived effect falls off with the

39

square of the distance. The velocity at which the pollution propagates enters into the equation because, when the velocity is very great, the pollution will always span the distance to the observer and be perceived; when it is low, the pollution may be dispersed or ameliorated before it can be perceived. The time between intervals affects perception inversely because widely spaced episodes tend to be forgotten.

There is no populated place where there are not some people who enjoy the environment, bad as it may seem to others. There are always some people who derive a living from it, bad as the environment of the region may seem in other ways. There is no shore region where there is not at least one commercial fishery: the question is how intense the fishery is. There are sports fisheries everywhere; there are animals everywhere; there is an environment to be polluted everywhere. But they are not all of equal importance, and the absolute approach fails to give any basis for priorities in development. But an approach like that of the acoustical engineers would provide such a basis. The important questions are how many people are involved, and how far away are they? How often does the insult occur and for how long does it occur? If we are going to build a platform within sight of a million people, a degraded environment may be perceived in daylight hours all the time.

The Bureau of Land Management of the Department of the Interior is trying now in a general way to take this kind of perceived exposure into account in its assessments. Of course, if we take all these factors into account, we may change our ranking of areas that might be drilled.

Where might we expect the maximum and minimum perceived environmental exposure from offshore drilling according to this formula? Consider the Gulf of Alaska which the Council on Environmental Quality recently identified as the least desirable for drilling. The environment there is relatively unfavorable because of storms and earthquakes, and pollution episodes may be relatively frequent, but during the next thirty years there will not be many people in range of any form of pollution. There are no more commercial fishermen there than in other places. Endangered species must, of course, be taken into account, but there are endangered species everywhere. The Gulf of Alaska, on this basis, might well be a relatively desirable place to drill: the perceived environmental exposure forecast would be relatively low.

Consider the Gulf of Mexico. The number of people is substantial in the region but most of the oil is far from land or off the sparsely populated Mississippi delta. Thus there is little perceived environmental exposure except when conditions favor rapid drift of oil slicks to the shore. Either drilling is far from land, or else (as off Louisiana) there are already a vast number of oil wells around. With relative environmental impact being considered, we can say that the "background noise" is already so great there that a small increase would not produce much effect. The PEEF for the next few decades in the gulf is therefore in the medium range despite the large number of offshore oil fields and a coexisting major fishery. Almost the same analysis applies to the proposed drilling on Georges Bank or elsewhere far out from the shores of the northeastern United States.

The perceived environmental exposure forecast anywhere off the East Coast or far off California would be in the medium range. Off the East Coast, the drilling would be a hundred miles from land. Some drilling off southern California would also be a hundred miles from land. The environmental hazards are reasonable and the pollution would be distant, even though the population along the adjacent coastal belt is enormous.

The PEEF for pollution resulting from drilling three miles off Santa Monica and Long Beach is clearly extremely high. Millions of people might perceive a degradation of the visual environment during daylight every day. Any oil spills would have a short trip to beaches swarming with people, and the most commonplace oil films and discoloration from suspended sediment around platforms would annoy countless surfers and sport fishermen. If the concept of perceived environmental exposure were applied, it is difficult to believe that these near-shore areas would be considered for leasing. The area off Santa Barbara is comparable, although the population is by no means as large and the PEEF before the 1969 spill would have been much lower than for Santa Monica Bay. Consider the perceived exposure from that one spill and the effect it has had on all subsequent development of the continental shelf. If the PEEF concept has merit, the last place to be drilled would be in sight of a populous recreational shore. Santa Monica Bay would be the last place off the United States that we should drill. I do not say we would never drill there, but it is the last place we would drill.

COMMENTARY AND RESPONSE

William Hargis

I have been asked to make some comments about the onshore impact of outer continental shelf oil and gas development. This is not a paper. My comments are based on recent experiences and evaluations both in the Commonwealth of Virginia and at the federal level; the National Advisory Committee on Oceans and Atmosphere, with which I am associated, has recently been evaluating some of the potential effects of OCS oil and gas at the request of the U.S. Senate. In the work that has been done, we have, of course, received statements about the need to develop these OCS resources. We have evaluated these statements as well as we could, and we have concluded that the United States at this time, for various reasons, does need to proceed with development of OCS oil and gas reserves. With different inputs, we might have concluded otherwise.

Having reached that conclusion, we believe that our responsibility is to evaluate the technical engineering aspects and the environmental aspects of OCS development—what do we know and what should we know? We have been concerned with evaluating the impact upon the resources themselves, since we cannot use them without depleting them, and when we deplete them, they are not usable by posterity. In addition, the environmental impact is important. Moreover, although this is not our primary responsibility, it has seemed to us that the economic conservation aspects of the problem need to be considered: dollars are, in fact, a national resource and, like the environment and natural resources that we propose to use, they should be preserved. We have also tried to look at some of the social costs involved.

The geographical areas involved in OCS development can be separated into three parts: offshore, near shore in the interface zone, and onshore. It is with the last two—that is, with the impact on the coastal zone—that I wish to deal here. The operations, as you have already heard, can be separated into exploration, seismic and coring activities, and exploratory drilling activities. None of these seem to have much potential for environmental damage. These preliminary activities are followed by development—that is, by bringing the fields into being—and then by the continuous production phase. One must also consider transportation requirements as a part of outer continental shelf development, since either ships or pipelines have to come ashore. There is also a need for storage tanks, pumping stations, and so on. Another aspect that has been previously mentioned is the

43

service activity required. All of these phases of exploration and development require services, and some—such as the port facilities—are extensive. All these latter phases of the activity do of course interact with the environment.

Contamination, occupation, and consumption of the environment are possible outcomes. Indeed, it does not seem possible to avoid partial contamination and it is certainly impossible to avoid occupation, by which I mean, for example, what would happen off the East Coast, in the Virginian Sea between Cape Hatteras and Cape Cod, when the potential oil fields do coincide with the productive offshore fisheries now being exploited heavily by U.S. fishermen and even more heavily by foreign fishermen. Obviously, one cannot install objects on the ocean bottom that will not interfere with trawling in some way if the fishery beds and the oil locations coincide.

We have generally concluded that offshore activities—and that is not my responsibility here though it was Professor Menard's—if properly conducted by competent operators with the proper data, will cause only slight environmental damage. We are concerned with the impact on fisheries by occupation and with associated naval problems, and there is, of course, the danger of blowouts and spills that can reach the coastal zones if conditions are right.

In our area, that is, from Long Island Sound to Cape Hatteras, these fields are relatively far offshore, and the presumed risk of oil spills from offshore, intersecting with the shoreline, as long as they are not large spills, is slight. The interface area—that is, at the beaches where the pipelines must be brought ashore—has been given some attention. The best estimates, based upon experience in the Gulf of Mexico, were recently presented by Dr. Miles St. Limeaux, who has responsibility for considering fishery problems in Louisiana. Dr. St. Limeaux believes that pipelines can be brought ashore without a great deal of environmental damage or hazard. The same thing would be true, I think, of some of the other activities that take place at the shore, that is, including vessel operations. It is across the surf zone—the interface zone—and out of the water that the major impact of offshore development is likely to occur.

As all of us are aware, research in the last two decades has indicated that wetlands and marshes are extremely important to the continuation of fishery resources, to the quality of water, to the protection of the land, and so on. Wetlands are a critical commodity, in short supply. Oil spills do affect wetlands. There is also a question, of course, how much will the oil spill affect the beaches. Those who walk on the beaches do not generally like to get dirty feet. Black sand, unless it is natural black sand, is not particularly attractive. The beaches of Virginia, of course, were coated for a long period with oil resulting from the torpedoing of tankers in Torpedo Alley around and below the mouth of the Chesapeake Bay. We have some experience with that problem. Incidentally, the long-term environmental consequences of those releases from the torpedoed tankers has not been great, as far as we can tell.

44

Particularly if platforms are involved—if there is actual drilling in the wetlands themselves or the near-shore environment (something we do not expect in the Atlantic, but which has occurred in the Pacific and the Gulf)—there will be chronic spills and occasional large spills, and their impact does have to be considered. We expect that in our area—that is, from Long Island Sound to Cape Hatteras— if the offshore oil and gas fields are proven and developed, our biggest strain will be from the development of services and facilities ashore—that is, from marshaling yards, docks, and harbors. There will also be some impact in the estuaries and tributaries themselves if dredging and soil disposal are necessary to establish and service offshore fields. By the way, fabrication plants do exist, in point of fact, at the tip end of Cape Charles on the eastern shore of Virginia. Brown and Root has acquired a number of acres and, if the Atlantic offshore is developed, the tip of Cape Charles will be a place for fabricating offshore structures.

Then there are the service facilities, which brings up the question of the availability of space for handling vessels and for the pipeline storage and pumping stations that will have to be installed in the onshore area. There may be refineries and such associated activity as petrochemical development, but these do not always accompany development of offshore fields, and on the East Coast we do have a fairly good supply of reserve refining capacity. There are, however, signs that even on the East Coast there will be some growth in refinery activity if offshore oil and gas is developed there.

There will have to be some growth, of course, because we need the energy. But all of these things can be handled if we have planned well enough for handling them, though I agree with Carl Savit that long-range planning is sometimes a delusion. Planning and organizing to handle these facilities requires our having the data and appropriate management systems. Unfortunately, in some of these areas the necessary information about the environment is not available in the quantities we would like to have. Dr. Menard, however, made a very interesting point: if we want to wait until we, as ecologists, are thoroughly assured that we know what we are talking about, we should be planning to wait a long time.

At the present, the belief of the National Advisory Committee on Oceans and Atmosphere is that we cannot afford to wait that long, and that we will therefore have to be satisfied with something less than complete understanding. Professor Menard in his paper mentioned a waiting period of two years; I would prefer to say three years, since I would like the statistical assurance that another year would give, though that assurance may be illusory. We do, however, need general baseline data, and that is being acquired. In the meantime, the National Advisory Committee has recommended that the leasing proceed in order that production take place as quickly as possible. But the committee has also recommended that the acquisition of baseline data go forward as rapidly as possible; once the leases are made it is expected that there will still be some reasonable period of time, say, eighteen to thirty-six months, before one has to consider imposing engineering requirements and environmental requirements on the developer.

One point that is clear is that in most of the East Coast states—I cannot evaluate California as well—there is not sufficient government apparatus to handle the onshore impact of things like pipeline corridors. In a good many of these states, land management is rather primitive: in fact, in the mid-Atlantic states zoning is almost ludicrous. This is one of the problems facing the coastal zone management program, and it is one that the secretary of commerce will have to deal with. It is also one of the problems that the states will have to deal with; it appears that we will have to grow up very rapidly. These areas have insufficient resources to handle the intense pressures that will come about in the development of resources to handle services, highways, and other infrastructure. This is particularly true of the area in Delaware from Cape Pendleton south to the mouth of the Chesapeake Bay. The states and localities need time to develop these resources and coastal zone management capabilities. Yet the energy need is real and there needs to be action.

One thing that must be included in any plan is adequate provision for oil spill prevention and for cleanup if spills occur. Another aspect that has to be considered is what is going to happen to the debris when the oil fields themselves are depleted. In Virginia, and here I am speaking as the adviser to the governor of Virginia, we considered the potential for development of suspected oil and gas reserves off the Baltimore Canyon Trough in the Virginian Sea, and we took considerable trouble to develop an evaluation and contingency plans for what we would do if in fact our claim to this hundred-mile territorial sea was honored. Unfortunately, eight old men made that work somewhat academic. Nevertheless, we are now better prepared to deal with the federal government than we were. The Virginia legislature last year passed a bill which, if the eight old men had not decided against us, would have applied certain controls to oil company operations.

John Devanney

Dr. Hargis will hear from my cartographer tomorrow. It may have been the Virginian Sea two weeks ago, but now it is the Department of the Interior Sound. Beyond that comment, I will be considering Dr. Menard's paper here. And first of all, I want to agree with him on the dubious value of baseline studies. Indeed, I would go further and assert that in the face of the notoriously high noise associated with biological systems, the marked variations and spatial densities, and the importance of long period cycles, most of what I have seen suggested for baseline studies represents a waste of resources. I believe that we will obtain little biological information in the vicinity of potential drilling. We have had a long-term and extremely large-rule experiment going on in the Gulf of Mexico for over thirty years. If that experiment has taught us anything, it taught us that if there is long-term serious damage from offshore production, it is not likely to be revealed by crash two-year field programs. After three years in the offshore production environmental impact game, I have come to the conclusion that the environmental trade-offs associated with offshore oil are weak.

For example, analysis of past spill statistics indicates that about the same amount of oil will be spilled from outer continental shelf wells as will be spilled from landing imported crude. We assume that the same amount of oil will be landed in either event and the net environmental impact for each on a national scale will essentially be the same. It should be emphasized that offshore oil can be cheap. Our work at M.I.T. over a three-year period indicates the resource cost to the nation of landed OCS oil can easily be less than $2.00 or $3.00 a barrel. A while back Secretary Morton put the resource cost of OCS oil in the vicinity of $2.00 or $2.50 a barrel. We think he was right. I have come to the conclusion that the real issue on offshore oil is who gets the economic gravy.

If the OPEC cartel should hold together, the net increase in national income from landing OCS oil rather than importing foreign crude could be as much as $7.00 to $8.00 a barrel recovered. I am not as sanguine as Professor Dorfman that the price will come down—but I think that the resource cost could be even less than what we have seen suggested this morning. In any event, if one believes the U.S. Geological Survey projections of 65 to 130 billion barrels yet to be delivered offshore, this resource may be worth as much as $500 billion net. Even if one prefers to believe Professor Dorfman rather than Professor Devanney, it may represent $100 billion in net increase in national income—a very large number, indeed.

Ms. Heller might be interested in a nonindustry, non-U.S. Geological Survey comment about onshore and tertiary recovery. We did a study of the Environmental Protection Act (EPA) recently, coming in as outsiders. I expected to find that there was a considerable quantity of oil still to be found and even a considerable quantity at present prices, but that is not so. The nonlinear characteristics of reservoirs mean that most of the oil that comes out will come out rather cheap, and then things will become very difficult very quickly indeed. A supply of oil from tertiary recovery—there has already been considerable secondary recovery—is going to be quite difficult to achieve and marginal in quantity. We agree with Mobil and others in putting the amount of new oil to be found onshore on the very low side—which, of course, makes the offshore oil that much more valuable.

The key question, in my opinion, is how this economic rent should be divided by the federal taxpayer, the coastal developer, and the state—as I said, who gets the economic gravy? In this area, I support Dr. Menard's call for public exploratory drilling, though in fact I am putting those words in his mouth. What I am talking about is a publicly funded and government-run program that would involve contracting the work out to the service companies that perform this function for the current leases. I would follow exploratory drilling with bonus bidding rather than the royalty bidding suggested by Dr. Menard in his paper: it is patently unreasonable to expect a private firm to pay for exploratory information and then to give it to competitors. If the information is kept within the government, as it is at present, then we still have the same barriers to competition. I am against royalty bidding in all its forms, because of the pernicious allocative effects associated with the gross alterations of the developer's marginal cost.

The reason I am for public exploratory drilling is that I am no longer confident effective competition exists among lease bidders. I am aware of the numbers— we worked them out ourselves at M.I.T.—which show that up to now the industry has not made much money on the OCS. However, the new factor here is the large increase in crude prices: the wide discrepancy between the landed cost of OCS oil and the landed OPEC price implies that for the important prospects— including most of those we have found in large fields—competitive lease bids should run into the hundreds of millions of dollars and more. Yet these same prospects can easily come up dry, as seen in the Destine Dome case, where Exxon bid $600 million for a tract in the Gulf of Mexico which produced only dry holes. We are faced with a combination of extremely high expected value with extremely high risk.

This is a game in which few can play, and even these few must join together in combines to spread risk, causing a further decrease in the number of bidders and, perhaps worse, the requirement for pre-bid communication among actual and potential combine members. Without our postulating collusive intentions on anyone's part we have nevertheless lost the two traditional requirements for effective competition among bidders. The plans of the Bureau of Mines for greatly increased leasing—that is, a large number of bidders and no pre-bid communication among bidders—though justified on national income grounds, will further exacerbate this problem. It would be only prudent on the taxpayer's behalf for us to suggest alternatives to the present system, since a lack of effective competition among bidders could easily result in the transfer of scores of billions of dollars from the taxpayer to the developer.

The best of the alternatives, in my opinion, is public exploratory drilling followed by bonus bidding. After exploratory drilling, the uncertainties on the amount and form of petroleum in each tract, including the basic reservoir parameters, would be very much less than before the tract was occupied. The problem essentially becomes one of bidding under certainty. Antitrust laws could be strictly enforced and combines made illegal. Any knowledgeable observer could compute the approximate value of the tract, and if the bidding were not at competitive levels, that fact would be apparent to all. Operators without a large capital base could take the results of exploratory drilling to financial institutions and make a strong case that for them to finance a bid at, let us say, 80 percent of the computed economic value of the tract would be a low-risk investment. Large oil companies would know this kind of financing was possible and be forced to maintain their bids at close to the zero net-present-value level.

Public exploratory drilling brings us the nice allocative properties of bonus bidding, while avoiding the breakdown of bonus bidding in the face of very high expected values for tracts combined with high levels of uncertainty. I realize that there are a number of nontrivial implementation problems with exploratory drilling, and that these may force me to percent-of-profits bidding. I look forward to the discussions over these two days.

L. P. Haxby

My remarks are not prepared, though I did have an opportunity to read Dr. Menard's paper. I would certainly like to agree with my three marine scientist associates, including Dr. Devanney. We, too, and our biologists believe that baseline studies are somewhat irrelevant. It is also true that we never stop collecting data. Everyone likes to acquire new data, but the idea of continually collecting baseline studies or baseline data from studies rubs us the wrong way. Among other things, it simply represents a delaying action, and we are not anxious to delay. We would like to suggest an alternative.

We believe that it would be reasonable to go into a new area and do what I would like to call a baseline survey or biological survey, just to give us some idea whether cats and dogs or whales and fin fish live there. Then as activity begins, it seems to us that we could take on a reasonable monitoring project in the area. If a disaster occurs—as it may in any location—that is when an incentive baseline survey or monitoring program could and should be implemented. There would always be an unaffected area close enough by so that comparisons of damage can be made. We put this forward as a positive suggestion, as an alternative to spending time and money finding out what is there today, since it will not be there tomorrow.

I would like to point out that some of the offshore areas we have been talking about are fairly nonproductive from a biological standpoint. The deep waters, basically, do not have the biological species developing in them that we are interested in, nor indeed the properties to support the particular forms of life we are interested in. Nevertheless, partly due to the effect of spills on sea life and partly due to their effect on the amenities, we are plagued with people talking about the terrible disaster of oil spills. We believe that during the last several years we have learned some things about handling oil spills and about the effect of oil spills. I would like to second Mr. Radlinski's remarks about the preventive effects. I think that the Environmental Protection Agency has put forth one of the most positive preventive regulations we have yet to see in its spill prevention, countermeasure, and containment plan. The developer must file notice of what he will do to prevent oil spills in his own shop; and if he has a spill, he must bring it in to the EPA for review, because it will then be obvious that his prevention plan has not worked. This is one of the better regulations we have seen. We appreciate an approach like that, and it is my understanding that offshore operators at the current time are embarked upon similar prevention measures. It may be that the environmental damage from spilled oil is not so great as we have believed. But about four years ago there was a number two oil spill in West Thelma, and afterwards Dr. Max Bloomer pointed out rather forcefully that the oysters and other marine life in the area had become heavily contaminated with hydrocarbons. Dr. Bloomer was quite right, and, among other things, he taught us that we should have been analyzing for hydrocarbons in marine tissue all along.

I would like to mention a program that the oil industry, through the American Petroleum Institute, has been carrying on for some four years now on the fate and effects of oil in the water. This is a long-range program and has spanned a large area: it studies what happens to oil when it gets on the water, the effects of partitioning, the effects of dispersion, the effects of evaporation, and so on. We have to admit that in a three-dimensional system there is not much well-defined knowledge where oil goes. It happens that Dr. Devanney has done some of the original single-dimensional modeling. That single-dimensional modeling is good enough on the surface, but which direction does the oil go from there? We have had several contractors, primarily universities, studying what happens to various types of oil, to various compositions, as they are exposed to marine animals.

At the present time we have contractors who have duplicated the work of other scientific organizations—Battelle, Northwest Laboratories, and Texas A. & M. Marine Laboratories. Their work has shown that nearly every species absorbs hydrocarbons when exposed to them; but then, when placed in clean water, the species quickly deprivate and lose the hydrocarbon. This bears directly on Dr. Bloomer's earlier work, since he said that the hydrocarbon did not come out of the tissue system. Since that time co-workers have found, first, that Dr. Bloomer's work was based only on the examination of three oysters and, second, that his test tank was contaminated with oil leaking from a pump during the deprivation experiment. Our work has gone through several hundred oysters, several hundred clams, several hundred shrimp, and so on, at each one of the investigative locations, and we believe that our findings are now fairly well documented.

Work has also been done on phyloplankton by Dr. Samuel Ray at Texas Marine Institute, and we have had examinations right here at Coal Oil Point of chronic oil exposure for abalone that have lived and grown up in this area. To date, we can find no evidence of tumor materials, carcinogenic materials, or what have you in the marine animals that are constantly exposed to Coal Oil Point oil.

50

Speaking of carcinogens, as Dr. Menard did in his paper, I would like to suggest that the mechanism for analyzing hydrocarbon or, particularly, for analyzing polynuclear aromatic hydrocarbons in marine tissue has been virtually unknown. There are at present only two laboratories that can test for polynuclear aromatics in this particular fashion, one being the Food and Drug Administration laboratory. The interesting thing is that in analysis of a mussel taken from the West Thelma area that is still reported to be contaminated, it was found that the level of polynuclear aromatic content in the mussel was less than one-half part per billion. To put that in perspective, the National Academy of Sciences Workshop on the Fate and Effects of Oil pointed out that lettuce, mushrooms, smoked meat, and so on all have polynuclear aromatic hydrocarbon contents ranging from four to forty parts per billion.

I think we must keep in mind that disasters will occur. We believe our record in the industry has been good. We have tried to make some progress in technology and in understanding what effects are occurring.

I would just like to close with one other little item directed at anyone who is really interested in oil spills and the fate and effects of oil. The Coast Guard, the American Petroleum Institute, and the EPA are holding a conference in San Francisco devoted to this subject alone for three solid days next week.[1] Not only will some excellent technical papers be given, but there is a commercial exhibit of oil cleanup containment equipment and so on. So this is an opportunity to see whether any progress has been made in cleanup technology and to see what is known about the fate and effect of oil.

Charles Matthews

Dr. Menard started out his paper by saying that more is known about the environment and the environmental impact of offshore drilling than anyone expected would be known. This would appear to reiterate the liturgy that we do not know all that there is to know about the marine environment or are dissatisfied with the available knowledge and so should delay development until more is known. I believe it is unrealistic to expect complete knowledge of all the conceivable implications of our actions before any actions are taken. If our energy resources were only as inexhaustible as the reservations some people have about adding to them, the nation would be in a position to tarry long enough for the coastal states to finish their plans for absorbing the onshore impact of offshore drilling, and there would be time enough to study the effective aquatic environment until it is as well understood

[1] Published as *1975 Conference on Prevention and Control of Oil Pollution Proceedings*, March 25-27, 1975, ed. Tom Nanney (Washington, D. C.: American Petroleum Institute, 1975).

as the surface of the moon—there might indeed be time to perfect such an infallible technology that it would be certified by Ralph Nader as being safe at any speed.

A little bit later, Dr. Menard referred to a danger that we will believe a few years of measuring ocean currents or other environmental variables represents a reasonable compromise between knowing nothing and knowing enough. He referred in his paper to these variable variations or rhythms of some sort, saying it will probably require five such rhythms or perhaps fifty years, half a century, before we know enough. Let me refer him specifically to the final report of the Gulf University Research Consortium, which is a group of some twenty universities, ranging from Mexico around the gulf to Florida. They have completed their report after several years of concentrated study. They conclude, "natural phenomena, such as seasonality, floods, upwellings, dwellings and turbid layers have a much greater impact upon the ecosystem than do petroleum drilling and production activities." Another one of their conclusions is that "Kimberly Bay has not undergone significant ecological change as a result of petroleum drilling and production since just prior to 1952, when other more limited baseline data were generated."

Dr. Menard goes on to point out the difficulty of knowing how much oil is out there. He says, "To my mind, the offshore estimates are an enigma," and argues it has been made abundantly clear that no one truly knows how much oil is out there until we go out and drill, stake out, explore, and delineate the size of the fields and the potential of production from those fields. He points out that at the present time we have secret exploration—a point Dr. Devanney also made. We are making major policy decisions to proceed or not to proceed in almost complete ignorance, and he calls for public exploration. Professor Dorfman mentioned this same point—that the public, meaning the government, does not know, does not have adequate information. Mr. Radlinski attempted to put the lie to that statement, so to speak. Let us have it understood now once and for all that the federal government knows everything that an oil company knows about what is out there: the government has the right to buy the data from the geophysical contractors. It is these results of the geophysical exploration that are available to the oil companies. How are these results interpreted? The other factors brought into the interpretation have little or nothing to do with the data upon which tract assessment can be made. These data are available. Let us stop this foolish repetition that the public does not know: they do know or they can know if the government will buy these data.

Professor Menard goes on to point out that there will be spills. There will always be spills. Now the recent report on petroleum and marine environment published by the National Academy of Sciences estimated that 6.1 million metric tons of petroleum hydrocarbons enter the oceans annually. More than one-third of that amount is from transportation, which takes into account tankers, drydocks, terminal operations, buildings, and accidents. The contribution of offshore oil production was estimated at only one-twenty-sixth of the amount put in by transportation. Natural seeps—or God's pollution or nature's pollution, whatever one wants to call it—put into the oceans eight times the amount of pollution that is put there by offshore production. The real national concern about spill risks should not center on the probability of incidents or the amount of oil that may spill, but the danger to our society if we, as a nation, let the emotionalism of the day deter us from taking the risk of offshore development.

Professor Menard points to the PEEF—the perceived environmental exposure forecast. I wish he had talked about that a little bit more, because it is a fascinating idea. Nevertheless, environmental exposure will not quite work the way acoustical exposure works, because petroleum is not where we want it to be, but wherever it is. When we talk about offshore drilling, we cannot say we will drill in a particular place because drilling there will have less perceived environmental impact than drilling somewhere else. We will have to drill where the oil is. The refineries, the onshore support that Dr. Hargis talked about, we can move around, but the PEEF is going to relate to offshore drilling, as Professor Menard pointed out. And we cannot move that wherever we choose.

One of the things that Professor Menard included in his evaluation was visual pollution. Remember, friends, that beauty is in the eye of the beholder. Now I do not like Picasso, though some people do. But I personally feel that an offshore drilling rig is a beautiful sight to behold. Now, an environmentalist may like Picasso, and he may not think an offshore rig is beautiful. But it is very difficult to measure the beauty of either.

Let me talk just a little bit about what Dr. Hargis said. First, Brown and Root will develop Cape Charles, and as I recall, the *Washington Post* and other newspapers around the East Coast have reported that the people around Cape Charles are thankful for this development. Cape Charles has been a depressed area: employment has been down, and the citizens of Cape Charles are looking forward with relish to Brown and Root's revitalizing the area. Dr. Hargis also mentioned the problem of planning for debris disposal after drilling is over. As I understand it, the current regulations of the Department of the Interior provide that once a drilling facility is no longer needed, it has to be moved fifteen feet below the mud line, and the bottom has to be dragged to make sure nothing is left there that will adversely affect the area. I think all the planning has been done. We have not yet had to abandon a platform, though there are some in the Gulf of Mexico that are almost ready to be abandoned.

My final point is that we must admit the energy supply situation demands development of the potential resources of the outer continental shelf. In our present situation, as we begin to think about our bicentennial next year, I can but be reminded of the ringing words of Patrick Henry, a fellow Virginian, to the Virginia convention on March 23, 1775: "Are we disposed to be among the number of those who having eyes, see not, and having ears, hear not the things which so nearly concern their temporal salvation." Let us see the truth. Let us hear the truth. Let us move on.

Francis Sarguis

I have enjoyed everything that I have heard, though I disagree with just about everything Mr. Matthews had said, in particular. I would say that visual pollution, although it is not in my mind the primary factor to consider, is certainly an important factor, and I think that there can be substantial agreement as to what constitutes unacceptable visual pollution. I would plead with the gentlemen here, to the extent they have anything to say about it, that unless it is absolutely a matter of national emergency and last resort, we not have oil derricks in a place like Yosemite Valley. We have presented this same argument on the Santa Barbara Channel, which is considered an intensely tourist-oriented area. Of course, we know that oil drilling offshore is probably inevitable. Wherever there is oil, it is going to be taken. But we believe there must be some priorities developed, considering, among other things, the visual pollution to which Mr. Matthews alluded. I do not find offshore rigs attractive.

I have prepared some remarks in answer to Professor Menard's paper. I would like to agree a little bit with Mr. Matthews in his reaction to the PEEF—perceived environmental exposure forecast—that Dr. Menard threw out, perhaps as a "wildcat" proposition. I agree that our present system for the selection of offshore drilling sites does border on the chaotic, but I believe that PEEF would fail to affect this situation to any meaningful degree. By Dr. Menard's own definition, PEEF would be based on perception, and I submit that it is neither realistic nor fair to allow perception to determine environmental effects.

The PEEF equation is a descendant of NEF, the noise exposure forecast, as Dr. Menard told us. I submit, and in part I agree again with Mr. Matthews on this, that under no circumstances can we reasonably compare the problem of offshore drilling effects to the problem of noise. One can only say so many things about noise, and they all come down to hearing and, perhaps, a few broken windows. But the effects of offshore drilling involve the possibility of oil pollution and the consequent degradation of the environment, even in the absence of a major spill. By Dr. Menard's own admission, there are extremely complex problems involved, with a multiplicity of variables, and they simply are not amenable to the simplification process implicit in PEEF.

I am also bothered by PEEF's implication that pollution, and more particularly perceived pollution, is what environmental degradation is all about. In other words, I am bothered by the view that while a certain low degree of environmental degradation might or might not pass PEEF muster in Santa Monica Bay because of its great population, it might be all right to have a very high degree of environmental degradation if it occurred far enough off shore. I have to question this as a very parochial and unjustified attitude. In the long term, I think it is very much in the public interest that such decisions take into account more than just the intensity of local population.

Dr. Menard's position, as I understand him, is that we simply do not know enough at this point to make conclusive and uncontested statements about the environmental effects of spills and such. He reminds us of the difficult tasks facing scientists, inasmuch as the different components of crude and refined oil produce different effects on various organisms, according to the climate and other environmental variables. Obviously, perception has a place in a quantification formula, but it is wrong, I think, to accord it the all-important role. The Q used to derive the PEEF formula refers to the quantity of pollution, but this Q must consider a multiplicity of other factors, not merely perception. What about the effects on the food chain? How long is the long range in considering carcinogens?

Mr. Haxby apparently thinks this is a matter of great public interest and concern, since he spent much of his few minutes assuring us that the American Petroleum Institute is studying this and is making some progress. I think that that in itself might be reason enough for delay and further study. What about the effect of oil on plant life and fish life? Is it not necessary to compile a full list of these effects? True, a great deal has been written on each of these subjects, but after all, the meaning of "ecology" requires us to interrelate all our knowledge, and it is in this interrelation that we have very often failed. If PEEF were broadened to take into account a number of the questions most of us want answered, we would definitely find an insufficiency of data at the present time, as Dr. Menard pointed out. But in the absence of life and death reasons, why should we bypass what is a very important stage of inquiry? Are we in such dire circumstances that we must rush headlong into these new offshore operations or suffer undesirable consequences?

I have read in newspapers, magazines, and elsewhere enough to convince me that we are not in those dire circumstances. We need the oil, but we do not have to do everything right now. Just what are the amounts of oil in these offshore areas? We do not even know the benefits we are going to derive. Who is correct in its estimates—the Geological Survey? National Science Foundation? American Petroleum Institute? Mobil Oil? This is vital information, and to the extent that the public might be enlightened by data accumulated by the private oil companies over the years, we should see that these data are made public. I remain to be convinced by Mr. Matthews to the contrary.

In my view, Dr. Menard in his paper takes too pessimistic a view of our ability to develop the necessary data quantification. I believe it can be developed over a reasonable period of time. I believe that once we have significantly expanded our information bank and have learned more about the stakes involved beyond private oil company profits (which we always are hearing about) we can hope for some intelligent decision making.

What constitutes an intelligent approach only our future decision makers can tell. The state of California has been working on a coastal plan. Sometime in 1976, the plan will, one hopes, be adopted by our legislature. It will contain many data and some specific goals for our own coastal zone management. Perhaps such a plan could serve as a model elsewhere.

Robert Solomon

As the last speaker on this environmental impact panel, rather than make a definitive statement on this issue, I would like to raise half a dozen questions. This environmental impact game—as Professor Devanney called it—is a game we have to play at the national level and at the state and local level as well. It is not an easy game to call and if we do not play the game right, the decisions will be made in the courts. As someone who has devoted a good part of his career to public policy analysis, I would hope that we can make decisions that are good enough not to require litigation and the delays that litigation involves. Although I once had an environmental lawyer tell me there is no such thing as an adequate environmental impact statement, I think there are two kinds of issues that, as public policy makers, we have to address: the legal issues and the scientific issues. Since the passage of the Environmental Protection Act in 1972, we have had to play this game very seriously. The outcome can be measured in some fairly hard economic terms that run into the hundreds of millions or billions of dollars. Environmental impact, per se, is perhaps more difficult to measure than are the dollars involved.

The first question I would like to raise in trying to judge an issue like the environmental impact of the offshore development is, What are we really looking for? Are we looking for quality of analysis or are we looking for comprehensiveness of analysis? I have read a good number of environmental impact statements for offshore development in the last few months on behalf of the state of California. Most of these documents are encyclopedic, but in my reading, totally unilluminating, being devoid of anything that I would really consider analysis. Now, what is the purpose of an environmental impact statement? Is it to fulfill a legal reporting requirement that leads us to write encyclopedias and to create a boom in the environmental consulting business, or is it to provide analysis that will be useful in decision making?

What kind of environmental analysis will be useful to a state or national public policy maker who has to say yes or no an hour later? As an example of the kind of analysis we have to evaluate, the Department of the Interior has just published a massive, 2,000-page, three-volume environmental impact statement for offshore

56

southern California. I think it is safe to say this statement fairly represents the current state of the art. The only real piece of analysis in this document is called a proximity analysis; it boils down to a tract-by-tract listing of how many miles the various tracts are from the various resources. This is what we used to call a single variable analysis, and it is not something I would like to hang my professional hat on. It is not something that would be useful to the public policy maker who has to say yes or no an hour later.

The second point I would like to make concerns the fact that we are talking about a national program that anticipates leasing practically the entire continental shelf of the United States. In each area, we must complete impact statements that are region-specific, site-specific, and tract-specific. Are we to strive for consistency of analysis in each of these documents, or will we try new approaches, or will we employ the latest state of the art in each one? Do we standardize? Do we freeze the technology with guidelines for the development of an impact statement, or do we try our best shot each time around? As public policy makers, we have to decide on some ranking of the relative risks and benefits in each of these areas. We have to make these decisions because, according to the latest information we have, there are still real-world constraints on capital, manpower, and various types of equipment to be used. There are real differences in the degree of risk that we face in these different areas.

Let me give an example of the public policy problem arising from this particular issue. When President Nixon first announced the acceleration of the outer continental shelf leasing program in the spring of 1973, he called on the Council on Environmental Quality to complete an analysis of the environmental risks of OCS development. Now, the resulting statement is one of the finest impact statements of all time, but it had one notable defect. While it considered development off the Atlantic coast and the Alaskan coast, it left out our particular problems in California. I was told this was done because California did not rank as a frontier area. So we did not have the benefit of the fine analysis that was done (among others) by the M.I.T. group.

The Department of the Interior impact statement shows the real difference between what can be done in one government agency and what can be done in another. In the decision-making matrix that is included in the Department of Interior impact statement on southern California, there is a column for relative environmental ranking according to the CEQ study. Unfortunately, there is no ranking for southern California in the CEQ study. How is a public policy maker to decide on this? Are we to attempt to re-create the kind of analysis that the CEQ did, or do we have to do without that kind of information?

The third question I would like to raise is, When we evaluate environmental impact, are we looking for systems views or simple views? Environmental impact is what planners call total environmental load. The problem is that in any one area, with the energy problems we have today, we are looking at impact statements on a variety of different projects. We have offshore oil and gas production; we have deep water terminals; we have liquefied natural gas tankers; we have various other proposed operations. If we were to read each of these impact statements separately, we would tend to conclude that the environmental impact of the proposed project was negligible and that the project should therefore go ahead. The question is, What happens when we add up all these impacts?

This is not a problem that cannot be solved. In fact, the Office of Technology Assessment of the United States Congress is sponsoring a systems study of what it calls "new use demands" for the coastal zones off the Atlantic coast. It is taking a systems look at offshore oil and gas development along with a look at deep water ports. There are some real advantages to this systems view. One advantage is that the critical bottlenecks and linkages that occur when these programs are combined seem to be eliminated when they are looked at together; whereas, if they are looked at separately, particularly if different agencies look at them, the total picture is likely to be lost. I did some research on this as it applies to Santa Monica Bay. I called the Southern California Regional Water Quality Control Board, for example, and staff people there told me they were mainly concerned about measuring the effects of sewage outfall effluents and could not judge the total water quality picture for Santa Monica Bay. If we need systems views rather than simple views, our decision-making process will change.

A related question is whether we are looking for specific impact or aggregated impact. It is one thing to make gross predictions based on spill probabilities and attempt to make predictions relating to the total volume of oil handled in an area. It is quite another to take the five separate bodies of water in southern California, and look at the circulatory system of each one along with the distribution of resources through that area. As I remember from my basic economics course, it is dangerous to make policy assumptions on highly aggregated information. So too in the program statements that we have, it is difficult to rely on such information.

A fifth question is whether on environmental and development issues we have integrated or sequential decision making. If I will consider y's permit application only after x obtains his application, that would be sequential decision making. The Coastal Zone Commission, as an example, will not rule on permit applications until all other permit applications have been obtained. Now, there is an issue here: do we want better decision making or do we want faster decision making? Our response in California has been to create the Energy Resources Conservation and Development Commission. We are trying to move forward with this idea on electric utility siting for "one-stop shopping." We believe that the one-stop decision is an advantage, not simply because it speeds up decision making, but because the benefit it offers of having the relevant state, local and federal agencies trying to evaluate the same facts at the same time.

58

The final point I would like to raise is this: Just as we have an ecological chain or a food chain, we have something I would like to call the technological regulatory environmental chain. That is, environmental problems are a combination of natural factors, technology, and the effectiveness of regulations. The best example of this lies in the fact that the exploratory drilling phase is generally considered to be the most hazardous phase of petroleum development, yet the safety record in this phase seems to be the best. I think there is a lesson here: when we look at natural risks, we must consider the available technology and the governing regulations. The greatest area of concern in California today has to do with the water depths that are proposed for development which are much greater than 200 meters. The average depth of the average tract just five miles offshore in Santa Monica Bay is 1,440 feet. The available technology and the regulatory obligations of both federal and state governments have to be considered together with the natural environmental problems in order to make an informed decision about drilling at such depths.

William Menard

I begin to see what I had not seen before—why it has not been my custom to write out my statements in advance. I think that Dr. Devanney and I are, more or less, in agreement: I do advocate public exploratory drilling, although I did not speak about it. As for Mr. Haxby, I just do not take notes rapidly enough to comment much on what he said, but I should point out that in mentioning the possibility of carcinogens in the food chain I tried to express my general doubt about our knowledge on the subject. Certainly our knowledge of biological effects is in considerable disarray because experts, including Max Bloomer and others, do not agree. On the other hand, as a nonexpert, I cannot properly exclude the possibility of such an effect.

With Mr. Matthews I did indeed run out of notes. I think there is some general misunderstanding of the intent of my paper. Though I did say that one cannot know everything about the environment, I did not say that we should therefore hold up all development. What I said was that one could judge it either way. As a matter of fact, Mr. Matthews said that because we cannot know everything, we should proceed to drill, and Mr. Sarguis said that, for the same reason, we should not proceed. Having raised this issue and prompted divergent views from people who are supposed to have divergent viewpoints, I think I did rather well in saying exactly what I did.

Mr. Matthews said the public knows exactly as much as the oil companies and that this issue should be laid to rest. The director of the U.S. Geological

Survey once told me that he had the authority to acquire all the information that the oil companies had, but that no one had given him the necessary money. Perhaps that situation has been rectified now, but as far as I know, it is not a question whether the federal government has legal authority to get information but whether it has the information. In any event, the main point I was trying to make is not that the federal government cannot learn as much as the oil industry. My point was that neither the government nor the industry knows very much about what is out there—that is, that both are ignorant. If they were not ignorant, they would come up with the same estimates on how much oil there is, and they do not.

Mr. Matthews made a statement with which I quite agree—namely, that most pollution is not from platforms. However, I took it that I was supposed to talk about the environmental effects of offshore drilling, not the environmental effects of something else. As far as I know from the National Academy of Sciences studies, most oil pollution off the United States occurs because people dump crank case oil into sewers and the like, or it results from spills in harbors, but it has nothing to do with offshore drilling. As far as I know, and I do not believe myself quite as well informed about this as about my last statement, there is and probably always will be far more pollution from tankers than from drilling offshore. An ordinary run-of-the-mill supertanker can hold as much oil as the Los Angeles Coliseum if it were filled to the brim. When we consider what that sort of a spill would do dumped into a harbor or almost any place, it is frightening. Judging by past spills, I find it had to conceive that such a disaster would result from oil drilling. However, I repeat, I did not think that I was supposed to talk about all the possible sources of pollution.

As to Picasso and platforms, I agree more or less with Mr. Matthews. I happen to like Picasso, or most of his work, and I do not happen to like platforms. Furthermore, I think the effort to disguise offshore platforms as high-rise buildings is ludicrous, since I do not like high-rise buildings either. But I agree that tastes differ. I have been accused of being cynical for suggesting that the oil companies might like to sustain an aesthetic group in this country who like offshore drilling platforms. There are people in England, for example, who wander through the countryside admiring old cast-iron bridges. At the time those bridges were built, people very likely thought they were hideous. Now there are people who like such things. Of course, I suspect most of the people do not like offshore platforms, and we have certainly heard from one person who does not. Let me turn to Mr. Sarguis.

I think that in trying to make a very simple statement about perceived environmental exposure forecasting, I may have deceived Mr. Sarguis as to my intent. My intent was that one would consider each different type of impact and add the different types together. Commercial fishermen, sports fishermen, pleasure boaters would perceive an impact if they operated in an area where there was drilling going on—but most of us are not rich enough to do that sort of thing, or we do not happen to make a living as commercial fishermen. It is those of us who are onshore that I focused on, and distance is quite critical for most of the phenomena that would result in visual (or any other) pollution.

I do not think that I attempted to answer Mr. Sarguis's question. Must we plunge headlong? The point I was trying to make was that, as Carl Savit said earlier, we have no way of knowing whether the important things are the ones we do know or the ones we do not know, and it is going to take some time to find out. My position is that those who favor or oppose drilling should take this ignorance into account.

Let me conclude here by saying I think Mr. Solomon is quite correct in emphasizing the legal as well as the scientific issues.

DISCUSSION

MS. HELLER: It is difficult to know where to begin. First of all, baseline studies have taken quite a beating today, and I would like to defend them. Several speakers have given the impression they believe that, because we cannot know everything, we should not attempt to know anything. That statement from reasonable people who would not say the same thing about the economy or virtually anything else they deal with seems to me to be outrageous. We have the example of the California sardine fisheries. What if the oil industry had been building up when the sardines disappeared? On the other hand, we have several environmental impact statements from the Department of the Interior which show the other extreme. The impact statement on a 10-million-acre-a-year leasing program had such scientific analyses as the statement that plankton population and production have not shown dramatic shifts in the Gulf of Mexico in twenty-five years, when, in fact, no one has monitored plankton population in the Gulf of Mexico for twenty-five years. We have a beautiful sentence in that environmental impact statement. The analysis of the effects of oil on marine mammals consists of the following: "We presume it will be negligible as long as the mammals are able to escape the area of the spill." That is a wonderful scientific analysis. I think it argues for a lot more study, which does not necessarily mean delaying things for fifty years to be able to recognize twenty-year cycles. I think there is too much effort to separate this into an either/or, black-or-white issue, where either we know everything or we know nothing. There is a lot we can learn by doing some relatively comprehensive studies.

One more point about environmental impact and baseline studies. A lot of people are tempted to make generalizations about background materials—for example, saying the fact that polynuclear hydrocarbons are found in lettuce and mushrooms and in the work at Coal Oil Point proves that oil really does not hurt anything. But there are a lot of background materials that are very damaging: arsenic, for example, is a background material, and we do not want to pour arsenic in the water. There are threshold limits, and it seems to me that these limits are what we really do not know about.

On the subject of public information, I must say I question the judgment of the gentleman who prefers oil rigs to Picasso. I would point out to him the fact that the Interior Department can buy data from the oil companies does not mean that the public knows the extent of the resources available. I think the question must also be raised whether it makes good sense to spend taxpayers' money on resources that are supposedly public resources to begin with. But there is a more important point: we are going into leasing before either the companies or the federal government knows what is there. It is partly a question whether the government knows or whether the companies know, but in fact I do not think anyone knows. What we are really talking about when we talk about federal exploration is our trying to get some idea of the extent of the resource so we can balance it against the environmental impact of developing it.

My last point is made in response to Dr. Devanney's statement. He plunged right into policy with the statement that the real policy question is who gets a share of the gravy. A few weeks ago he said that Massachusetts should say it would accept OCS development for a percentage of the lease payments. But if the state does not get that percentage, it should use environmental and legislative roadblocks to prevent the development.

I am a fairly strong environmentalist, but I would have to disagree with that. I think that when it comes to these policy questions, we can find some medium run in which development should take place. The question is how to balance the interests involved in offshore development. I would hope that the environmentalists' interests would be given as much credence as the other interests.

MR. KNECHT: I have been a little disappointed that we have not had much material on onshore impact presented here. I think the onshore impact of offshore drilling will be substantial. I am hoping that in the short time I have this afternoon I will be able to go into this further from the standpoint of coastal zone management. But my main point here is to comment on the baseline program, which I, too, think has been dealt with shabbily so far. Clearly, throwing money at the problem is not the answer. We have seen some sign that throwing money has been the response so far. Clearly, two years' research is not enough, but it is a beginning. I agree with Ms. Heller, if we had twenty years' or thirty years' worth of observations in the Gulf of Mexico, we would not have to rely on the two-year study that Mr. Matthews mentioned earlier to show what has happened in the gulf. I think we missed opportunities in the Gulf of Alaska, at least in Cook Inlet. There has been activity up there for the last seven or eight years, and I do not believe there is an ongoing and well-designed monitoring program there to tell us about oil effects in cold water. We had the opportunity and we missed it. In Milford Haven, in contrast, a very modest study has been under way for ten or fifteen years, since that port developed into the second largest oil port in the world. Those studies begin to give, I think, a relatively long baseline.

What is needed here is some careful thought about the levels of environmental information that we ought to have for the three key decisions that have to be made. The first decision is whether to lease, where to lease, and under what kind of stipulations. What is an adequate level of information at that point? We ought to study that problem and reach a consensus on it. Secondly, what do we have to know environmentally at the time a development plan is approved? Has the field been discovered, have the resources been mapped, and has the industry been able to locate production platforms, pipelines and onshore facilities? What kinds of environmental information ought to be on hand at the time of that key decision? Thirdly, what kinds of environmental information do we need when we approve production and allow it to continue over the lifetime of the field? I think we ought to get to the careful analysis of environmental realities. I envision a kind of baseline or assessment program that would continue over the life of the activity. It would begin as soon as possible, but it would continue through the lifetime of production.

PROFESSOR HARGIS: Dr. Devanney did jump on baseline studies rather hard, though with some justification. On the other hand, I disagree with his conclusion. We are always better off with some information than none; and, properly conducted, baseline studies can elucidate considerable relevant physical, chemical and physiological data. They will elucidate less in the way of biological data, except in the gross sense, though sometimes it does help to know whether there are large populations of some exploitable species, albeit that is only one aspect of a good biological survey. But I regard baseline studies as only part of a continuing environmental review and analysis that has to be carried on with the OCS oil and gas as well as any other activity that could have a marked effect on the environment. I regard baseline studies as the first stage, tract- and site-specific studies as the second stage, and continuing studies at the monitoring and research levels as the final stage. There should be an appropriate arrangement in the lease specifications for changing requirements, structurally and operationally, if continuing studies cause us to conclude that something is happening that we did not suspect and that we do not want to have happen. I think that continuing ecological evaluation, even basic research, is a necessary part of any activity like this, and I think it needs to be included in the cost of the production.

I do not, however, believe that we have to wait for ten, fifteen, or twenty years. I personally am convinced of the need for drilling, and I think that we ought to proceed on parallel courses—that is, we should proceed with exploratory leasing, while beginning the environmental analysis. Let drilling go forward, with appropriate provisions for adequate controls based on the information at hand when the time comes to grant a lease permit.

I believe it was Mr. Haxby who talked about the productivity of estuary areas, and, I think, implied that shelf areas are not very productive. That is not an accurate analysis. I would point out that the major parts of the Grand Bank and the Georges Bank would be construed to be on the continental shelf, as would be

65

the major fishery grounds in the mid-Atlantic. Indeed, coastal waters and the continental shelf waters are both productive, and that has to be taken into consideration. They yield considerable income from what are self-renewing resources when properly handled. That has to be figured into the economic calculations.

Mr. Matthews said directly that the Brown and Root operation at the lower tip of the Eastern Shore has been received with open arms. That is not a correct statement. It has been received with open arms by some, and it is being violently fought by others; indeed, the population as a whole has not yet decided if it is going to accept Brown and Root. In the last analysis, I suspect it is a tempest in a teapot, but it is a problem there.

MR. RADLINSKI: Mr. Chairman, there have been a number of statements that require a response, but there will not be enough time for a response.

PROFESSOR MITCHELL: I think that we can handle some of them this afternoon. If you do not have time this afternoon, then I think a statement ought to be submitted for the record. But I think we will have the time, because the topics this afternoon really encompass everything we have been talking about this morning.

PROFESSOR DEVANNEY: I have been misunderstood by both sides. It is not that I am against all baseline studies; I am against the design of these studies and what they are being sold as. If we have $15 million to spend on offshore oil environmental studies, the stuff that we are coming up with in these baseline studies would still not be what we want. Look at the record for the MAFLA study. And Mr. Matthews misunderstood my point completely: I was not talking about geophysical data; I was talking, as the others were, about exploratory drilling. The question that I was raising was, Is competition being maintained in the face of the uncertainties that both the government and the companies face when they have to bid before exploratory drilling?

MR. MATTHEWS: I am not going to answer either one of these. I want to make my comment to Dr. Menard. I thought my role was to comment and to criticize some specific points. I thought Dr. Menard did an outstanding job, and my compliments to him.

PART THREE

The Social Benefit/Cost Analysis of Offshore Drilling

Professor Walter Mead began the afternoon session by reporting that his analysis of the 1969 Santa Barbara oil spill had determined its social cost to be $16.4 million, a small amount compared to the value of the oil found. Professor Mead urged that government regulations imposed on oil companies to prevent spills themselves be subjected to similar analysis to see if their benefits outweigh their costs, since ultimately the public pays for them. Those listening to Professor Mead were at odds on whether his study of the Santa Barbara spill had measured the social costs fully and whether the cost of spills is tolerable. It was noted that coastal communities oppose offshore drilling because, while they bear most of the environmental costs, they receive few of the benefits of drilling. Another point made was the need for state management programs to deal with the onshore impact of offshore drilling.

SOCIAL BENEFIT/COST ANALYSIS OF OFFSHORE DRILLING

Walter Mead

The present discipline of economics has its historical roots in what was called political economy a couple of centuries ago. Modern economics has become increasingly quantitative, analytical, and rigorous. Today, economics offers an increasingly large number of tools useful in analyzing economic problems such as offshore drilling. Yet the public policy problems that government must resolve are still political as well as economic problems.

Public policy formation in the economic area has come a long way in the last few decades and still has a long way to go toward more efficient use of the scarce resources that are available. The fact that people like Darius Gaskins and Jack Carlson with their excellent professional qualifications can be appointed to high-level policy-related positions in the Department of the Interior is testimony to the progress that is being made. The challenge for the future is in two areas. First, some of our analytical tools are still primitive and need additional refinement. Second, public policy decision makers need to know that these analytical tools are available and need to understand how they may be used to improve the decision-making process.

While there has been considerable improvement, the decision-making process at the moment still reflects a distressing influence of powerful pressure groups whose interest is often in conflict with the general welfare. As a striking example, both the U.S. Senate and House of Representatives recently passed by very large majorities an act known as the Oil Transport Bill. This act would have required that by 1977, 30 percent of all oil imported into the United States be (1) transported on ships constructed in the United States, (2) owned by American companies, and (3) operated by American crews. This legislation would have further increased the price of oil to the American consumer, who would have been required to transfer some of his income to the three favored groups listed above. Except for a successful veto by President Ford last December, this act would have become law. It represents a near triumph of special interest group politics over the general welfare. The costs in resource misallocation would have been enormous and would have been borne by the general public.

Benefit/cost analysis is one tool of economic analysis which is capable of shedding a great deal of economic light on policy alternatives faced by public decision makers. The tool would appear to be extremely valuable in analyzing choices concerned with offshore drilling in particular. In order to clarify the meaning of benefit/cost analysis and to show how it may be used it will be helpful to start with a process known to every businessman—the process by which ordinary business investment decisions are made.

Managers of successful modern corporations commonly analyze investment alternatives available to them by determining the internal rate of return generated by alternative investments. Estimation of the rate of return requires (1) that the amount of the required investment be determined, (2) that operating costs be estimated over time, and (3) that the income stream to be generated by the investment be estimated. By subtracting outlay from income by years and discounting the differences to the present, an internal rate of return can be estimated for each investment under consideration. The well-managed corporation will then allocate its scarce capital funds among alternative investment possibilities in a way that maximizes the overall rate of return to the company. Capital thus flows to its highest yield. This process produces profit maximization for the firm and also produces social benefits by allocating scarce resources in ways that serve the needs of consumers.

However, occasionally "market failure" occurs when there is not a harmony of interest between private decision making and the social welfare. More specifically, the problem of "externalities" arises. An externality occurs when some of the costs resulting from a given business investment are borne by society but not by the firm responsible for the decision. Similarly, benefits may accrue to society and cannot be captured by the firm making the required investment. In this event, there will be underinvestment by private firms.

A classic illustration of an external cost is the problem of environmental pollution. Until recently a factory might pollute everyone's air at no cost to itself. The costs were borne by society but not by the firm. Increasingly the externality of air pollution has been subjected to regulation or penalties that have tended to reduce the discrepancy between estimated private and social costs.

In general, market failures resulting from either external costs or benefits are probably not large. In most cases there appears to be a high degree of correspondence between private costs and social costs, and between private benefits and social benefits. If this is true, then private decision making would also serve to promote the general welfare.

On the other hand, where the amount of the externality is large, corrections may take any of three forms. First, the government may by regulation control the amount of external costs forced upon society. This is now commonly done for both air and water pollution. Second, as an alternative to regulation, a tax or fee may be levied on the producer of an external cost, which in effect "internalizes the externality"—imposes a charge on the person or firm responsible for the externality equal to the value of the external cost. Third, where there is an important external benefit, a subsidy may be paid to the producer in an amount roughly equal to the value of the external benefit.

Shifting from private decision making to government decision making, we are confronted with a similar problem. The economic problem which confronts every nation whether capitalistic, socialistic, communistic, or other, is that it has available to it scarce resources available to satisfy the demands of its population. If these scarce resources are used efficiently, then the standard of living of the population will be relatively high. On the other hand, the standard of living will be unnecessarily low if either private individuals or governments allocate resources to low-yielding or even negative-yield investments. The resources that are allocated are society's resources whether the decisions are made by private firms which have control over them or by government organizations which have control over public resources. The principal difference between private and government investment decision making is that the government, if it correctly represents all of the people, should consider all costs and all benefits—that is, should internalize externalities. The costs that a government decision-making unit should consider are social costs and the benefits that it should consider are social benefits, whereas private firms normally make their judgments on the basis of private costs and benefits. The governmental decision-making unit should ask about the social rate of return whereas private business asks about the private rate of return. In most cases (labor cost, cost of materials, depreciation of machinery, and so on), the numbers should be the same. Where there are externalities, the numbers will be different.

In the case of offshore drilling, the predominant issue currently is not a matter of public investment but rather a matter of *preventing* private offshore drilling or *approving* and regulating such activities. But the analytical process is approximately the same. When the choices are identified, benefits and costs associated with each choice must be estimated.

The goal of public policy decision making can be concisely stated as follows: *The government should follow that decision which maximizes the present value of net social benefits.* The reference here to present value acknowledges that future net values are worth less than present net values. This follows from the fact that investments made today normally yield both a return of capital and an additional benefit in the future. To maximize present value is to choose that alternative which yields the highest social rate of return when all costs and benefits are considered.

The methodology for applying benefit/cost analysis to government decision making for offshore oil operations is similar to that identified above for private decision making. First, the social value of the investment must be estimated. Second, the social costs of operations over time must be identified. Third, the stream of social benefits that flows from the investment must also be estimated. Fourth, with these data determined, the internal social rate of return must be estimated for each of the alternatives under consideration.

71

The balance of this paper will be concerned with identifying some of the problems and booby traps that will be encountered and that must be understood by the decision maker in social benefit/cost analysis. In general the benefits and the costs must reflect real social values and must be corrected for a variety of distortions that may occasionally appear.

(1) *Monopoly distorts prices.* The essence of monopoly is that output is restricted in order to obtain artificially high prices and monopoly profits. In evaluating an offshore drilling problem, one must determine the value of oil produced from any operation. Historically, there was a reasonably effective private cartel known as the Seven Sisters that apparently was able to exercise considerable market power in the international oil industry. Today, there are at least 100 oil companies, including some that are government-owned, operating in the international oil industry.[1] This private cartel is now effectively displaced by an intergovernmental cartel, the Organization of Petroleum Exporting Countries (OPEC). As of November 1974 OPEC members accounted for 53.4 percent of the total world crude oil production. The Arab members of OPEC demonstrated their control over the world oil market by enforcing an embargo during the 1973–1974 Arab-Israeli war. The embargo ended in March 1974 and OPEC governments, through control over their output, have been able to avoid anything more than a $2.00 per barrel decline in prices. Today there is clearly excess productive capacity among OPEC members. This is a standard characteristic of a monopoly. Prices are currently above their competitive level and the existing output restrictions are proof of the point. An evaluation of benefits from U.S. offshore oil drilling must be based on an estimate of the true value of oil (the value which would result from effective competition between buyers and sellers) as opposed to monopolistic prices.

(2) *Uncompensated externalities also cause price distortions.* If production of a commodity imposes on society costs that are not considered by the firm responsible for them, then prices will fail to reflect true social costs. In the case of oil production, oil spills such as occurred in the Santa Barbara Channel early in 1969 clearly impose important costs on society, especially on the adjacent communities. The social cost of the Santa Barbara oil spill, including costs borne by Union Oil Company and its three partners, have been estimated at $16.4 million. These costs are itemized in Table 1. The principal element of social cost was beach cleanup, oil well control efforts, and oil collection efforts, totalling to $10.5 million. The other significant social cost was recreational value lost, estimated at $3.2 million. The total social cost of $16.4 million is a relatively minor item when considered against the value of the oil discovered.

---

[1] *Oil Import and Energy Security: An Analysis of the Current Situation and Future Prospects,* Report of the Ad Hoc Committee on the Domestic and International Monetary Effect of Energy and other Natural Resource Pricing, Committee on Banking and Currency, House of Representatives, 93rd Congress, 2nd session, September 1974, p. 48.

Table 1
ESTIMATE OF THE ECONOMIC COST OF THE
SANTA BARBARA OIL SPILL

Item		Estimated Costs (in dollars)
Union Oil Company on behalf of itself and three partners—Gulf, Mobil, and Texaco:		$10,487,000
Beach cleanup	$4,887,000	
Oil well control efforts	3,600,000	
Oil collection efforts	2,000,000	
U.S. Department of the Interior		382,000
State of California		200,000
County of Santa Barbara		57,200
City of Santa Barbara		negligible
Damage to tourism		negligible
Damage to commercial fishing industry		804,250
Property value loss		1,197,000
Fish life damage		negligible
Bird life damage		7,400
Seal and sea lion damage		negligible
Intertidal plant and animal damage		
Low estimate		1,000
High estimate		25,000
Value of lost oil		130,000
Recreational value lost		3,150,000
Low estimate		$16,415,850
High estimate		$16,439,850

Source: W. J. Mead and P. E. Sorensen, "The Economic Cost of the Santa Barbara Oil Spill," *Santa Barbara Oil Symposium,* December 17, 1970, p. 225.

That Union Oil Company on behalf of the four firms involved accepted the cleanup burden and that suits are under way or have been completed to recover additional private and social damages suggest that most and possibly all of the social costs of the oil spill will eventually be borne by the operators. Any subsequent offshore oil operations will most likely reflect the lessons learned from this incident and future private cost calculations will include the contingent costs of an oil spill. This requires that contingent costs including cleanup, loss of oil, and settlement in damage suits be estimated. Similarly, the government must include the probable social costs of an oil spill in its own decision making on both approval and regulation.

As the government attempts to avoid oil spills by means of its own regulations, it imposes costs on the operators and social costs on society. Thus, regulations issued as a means of avoiding a spill should also be cost-justified. It should be shown that the probable benefits from reducing the probability of an oil spill and reducing the probable damages if one should occur exceed the costs of complying with the regulations. I know of no evidence that the government has made such an evaluation. In the case of the trans-Alaskan pipeline, regulatory safeguards have been introduced that appear to have added at least $1 billion to the cost of the pipeline. It is not clear that the government has inquired about corresponding benefits and their values. To the extent that regulatory costs are added in excess of probable benefits, resources are unwisely allocated and living standards are unnecessarily reduced.

(3) *Private costs are not always social costs*. Some of the costs incurred by oil companies in offshore operations are borne by the operating companies but are not social costs from society's point of view. For example, bonus and royalty payments clearly reflect cost to operating companies. From society's point of view, however, they represent only transfers of money from oil companies to the government or private owners of oil resources. They are economic rents and not social costs.

As another illustration, data on motel occupancy during and after the Santa Barbara oil spill clearly indicate a loss of motel business by Santa Barbara beachfront motel operators. However, evidence also indicates that motel business improved in cities both north and south of Santa Barbara. Thus, society suffered no significant loss of motel services. The losses sustained by the Santa Barbara motel operators appear to have been offset by the gains of their competitors in other areas and the social loss was small relative to the private loss. Where oil companies are forced to compensate the motel operators who suffered losses and where the companies are unable to recoup such costs from motel operators who benefitted, the cost to the oil companies is a private but not a social cost.

(4) *Government intervention in the market may distort prices*. The field price of natural gas moving in interstate commerce has been controlled by the Federal Power Commission since 1954. The effect of this price control has been to hold natural gas prices below their competitive level. Effective January 1975, the Federal Power Commission permits a maximum charge of 51¢ per thousand cubic feet for new gas contracts. At the same time, gas is being imported from Canada at a price of $1.00 per thousand cubic feet. Further, liquefied natural gas is being imported from Algeria at a cost of about $1.50 per thousand cubic feet. A recent study of the effect of phased deregulation of natural gas prices indicated that equilibrium of supply and demand under free market conditions could be established by 1979 at a "real price" of 61¢ per thousand cubic feet (1971 dollars).[2] This price, of course, should be raised to reflect the effects of inflation.

[2] P. W. MacAvoy and R. S. Pindyck, "Alternative Regulatory Policies for Dealing with the Natural Gas Shortage," *Bell Journal of Economics and Management Science,* Autumn 1973, p. 489.

Under current price controls there is a shortage of natural gas. At artificially low prices, consumers demand more than suppliers are willing to produce. The current regulated price of natural gas does not indicate the true value of the gas. Gas is a joint product with oil in most situations. Thus, the benefits of offshore drilling will be understated if current prices of natural gas are used in the estimations.

Similarly, the price of crude oil is controlled in the United States by the Federal Energy Administration. "Old oil" is currently controlled at $5.25 per barrel while free market oil, accounting for about 34 percent of total domestic supply, has a market price of about $11.00 per barrel. The government price control system has distorted the price mechanism.

In addition, subsidies granted to an industry will normally increase supply and cause price to be lower than it would be in the absence of a subsidy. For the oil industry, tax subsidies exist in the form of percentage depletion allowances and intangible drilling cost expensing provisions. One scholar has estimated that income tax benefits for the oil industry have caused the domestic price of oil historically to be about 12 percent below what it would have been in the absence of such subsidies.[3]

From 1959 through May 1, 1973, import quotas were in effect, limiting the amount of foreign oil that might be imported into the United States. The effect of this restriction on supply was to cause the domestic price level to be above the level that would have prevailed in the absence of such restrictions. From the mid-1930s through 1972, market-demand prorationing frequently introduced artificial restrictions on oil and gas production with the effect that prices were again artificially high.

In view of these government interferences with the price level, we cannot take the market price as an indicator of the true value of oil. As a result, we must use what have been called "shadow prices" in lieu of observed prices. Shadow prices are simply an alternative estimate of the true value of the resource. Of necessity, these estimates are highly subjective but they probably represent improvements over prices distorted by various nonmarket influences.

(5) *New technologies normally will lower costs in the future.* In estimating future revenues we must consider probable new technologies that will have the effect of increasing productivity and lowering costs. There currently is no U.S. oil shale industry. When the first production plant comes on stream it is likely to be a relatively high-cost plant. Experience will be gained rapidly and second- and third-generation plants are likely to profit by the experience of predecessor operations. New technology comes rapidly in new industries. Rapidly declining costs have been demonstrated in such new industries as nylon, rayon, and desalination.

[3] G. M. Brannon, *Energy Taxes and Subsidies* (Cambridge, Mass.: Ballinger, 1974), p. 39.

The development of new safety devices that reduce the probability of oil spills will likely improve with the passage of time. However, it may be necessary to suffer additional oil spills in order to gain technological improvements in this area. Simply shutting in production does not necessarily obtain these benefits and is in fact likely to delay their availability.

(6) *Economic evaluation of costs and benefits is difficult.* Indeed quantification of some cost and benefit areas is extremely difficult, bordering in some cases on the impossible. The tools of economic analysis available for quantification have improved. Nevertheless, in some areas evaluation remains highly subjective. In other areas the probable range of estimates may be so great that quantification becomes virtually meaningless. A case in point arises with the possible losses from a major accident in a nuclear power generating plant. Within the context of offshore oil, the quantification problems are more manageable. In some areas where quantification problems are involved, the magnitudes may be relatively minor so that errors are of little consequence. For example, in evaluating the social costs of the Santa Barbara oil spill, evaluation of bird losses was not possible. However, whether the birds that perished as a result of the oil spill were assigned a value of $1.00 or $10.00 per bird made no difference when the total cost was rounded off to the nearest $100 thousand. Where uncertainty exists as to the range of values, a sensitivity analysis can be added whereby the effects of alternative estimates are shown.

In conclusion, use of benefit/cost analysis to evaluate alternative government policies on offshore drilling offers the policy maker and the legislator an opportunity to appraise economic values resulting from choices under consideration. In a democracy, public decisions are going to be heavily influenced by political forces. It should nevertheless be of considerable value to know the costs that are being imposed on society or the benefits which will accrue to society as a result of alternative political decisions in the economic area.

COMMENTARY AND RESPONSE

E. J. Cahill

By and large, I am definitely in accord with Dr. Mead. However, I would like to take exception to one item in his paper: that is, his reference to the earlier effective private cartel known as the Seven Sisters, which apparently was able to exercise considerable power in the international oil industry. I think history, at least the history of the last ten or fifteen years, indicates that no such private cartel really existed.

Dr. Mead's paper emphasizes the real need for a careful appraisal of both costs and benefits of any undertaking like offshore oil drilling. Federal regulations, of course, require that benefit/cost statements accompany environmental impact statements. I would like to emphasize that Dr. Mead has made a comprehensive and careful appraisal of both the costs and the benefits of the Santa Barbara oil spill on a rational basis, not an emotional basis. This rational analysis is a critical necessity if we are going to continue developing our economy and at the same time continue to improve our environment. My personal feeling is that both of these are worthwhile and necessary objectives.

Dr. Mead's $16.4 million figure for the cost of the Santa Barbara spill is significant. Considering that the effects of the spill were temporary and that the odds of such spills occurring are very low (given the history of offshore operations in this country), although their effect on the local environment may be significant, it would appear that the costs are acceptable from the national standpoint.

To justify that statement, we need to look at the benefit side of the equation. Let us take the southern California outer continental shelf as one example. According to the U.S. Geological Survey the reserves there are substantial. We hope that the drill bit will prove them to be substantial. Production from the region will be a significant offset to the imports that would otherwise be needed by this country. We are all aware that most of the reputable and unbiased authorities look for a continuing need for oil imports into this country for at least the next ten years and possibly indefinitely. Through offshore drilling we are, in a sense, internalizing a benefit, rather than sending payments out to foreign governments.

One critical point is that, in effect, we are trading offshore oil development, and its possible environmental impact on a local region, for (as an example) coal development and its possible serious environmental impact on some other region. One wonders if a coastal state really has the right to preclude the development of a needed resource. Obviously, doing so would be to the general disadvantage of the country as a whole. Certainly, at the very least, it would shift the burden of environmental impact to some other area. In this country the individual states are highly interdependent on one another for energy and for many other things. Regionalism—one might say localism—really cannot be tolerated, but there have been some unfortunate straws in the wind. For example, the Texas Senate passed very handily a measure that would prohibit the export to other states of new Texas gas found on Texas state-owned leases.

Finally, I would like to endorse the suggestion that the economic and social effects be considered with due regard for national as well as regional needs and with due regard for the serious hazard of delay until environmental regulations are adopted, whether by national or regional agencies. I think this would be entirely consistent with the present requirement that an environmental impact statement be filed when projects like offshore oil development are under consideration.

Darius W. Gaskins, Jr.

I would like to compliment Dr. Mead on his paper, and I would like to raise three major issues that I see there or that should be there.

First, while I am sympathetic to Dr. Mead's suggestion that the proper objective in handling our OCS resources or any other resources is maximization of the present value of the net social benefits, I would like to point out that there is no national consensus on that issue. There is in fact very substantial disagreement about who gets the economic rent. To put it bluntly, the problem is that oil is an extremely valuable resource from the national point of view but states and local communities believe they bear some of the costs, whether social costs or not, of the extraction of this resource, and, to the extent they have the ability to block or delay extraction, they will. It is obvious that our system has not accepted the notion that maximizing the present value of net social benefit is our objective. I say I am sympathetic to this objective because I, too, am an economist. But I am also sympathetic to the states whose tourist industries are threatened. It would be silly for us to ignore the fact that there are individuals and local communities that believe they are going to have to bear the costs of an enterprise whose benefits they do not receive. I certainly hope that the administration and Congress can somehow work out an arrangement whereby the individuals who are adversely affected are somehow compensated.

Earlier we heard seven people say they were in favor of a government oil exploration program. The argument that I heard for this program was that it would prevent a giveaway of resources. Now, if we accept Professor Mead's objective function, the possible giveaway of resources would not be an interesting question: it would not make any difference whether we gave the oil to the oil industry or whether we sold it to them for top dollar. In either case, we would maximize net social benefits. But I think it would be naive to say there is not tremendous interest in Washington and in this country generally about who in fact does get that economic rent.

On the other hand, it has been widely (and unfortunately) held that the economic rent is the only thing that matters. In fact, some have taken the position that rather than let the oil industry capture one single dollar of the economic rent, they would rather not sell the resources at all. There is a potential trade-off here between the benefit of developing the resource and the cost of possibly misallocating the benefit. But I do not know of any social utility function that says the trade-off is one dollar for one dollar (I hope it is not that high) or indeed any social utility function defining the trade-off: it is an issue we all have to work on together.

The Department of the Interior has been working to move ahead with the leasing program and, at the same time, capture the economic rent for the government. Whenever we face the question of accepting or rejecting a bid, we see the dilemma in its clearest form. If we reject a bid, we delay development of a needed resource. If we accept a bid, there is some chance we are giving away some of the economic rent to the oil industry. I think we all should be aware of this unresolved dilemma, and I think there should be a national discussion of exactly where we want to come out.

The second important issue that Dr. Mead raised was the cost of regulations and here I am in almost complete agreement with him. I heard earlier from a member of the panel that we should always use the best available technology. Now to say that to an economist is like waving a red flag, because, as I understand it, the best available technology means the technology that minimizes the possibility of an accident. If we consider the best available technology for getting to work, we will find that the best available technology for getting to work in the morning may be to work at home or else go to work in an armored truck, because every time we go outside the door, we stand some chance of being run over by a car. Obviously, there may be high costs to using the best available technology, and these should be taken into consideration.

It is naive to talk about best available as though it were costless. It will cost us something to improve technology, and we have to make a social trade-off between how much we wish to improve the technology and how much we want to spend. To tie this in with the issue of economic rent, let me say it is fairly obvious that if we have a competitive or nearly competitive auction while stricter and stricter regulations are put on the development of OCS tracts, the result will be that bonus rent and royalty payments—the economic rent captured by the federal government—will in fact reflect the higher costs: that is to say, they will decrease.

Ultimately, the federal government—which means the taxpayers—will pay for the strict regulations.

The third issue (which I think Professor Mead in fact slipped over) is that in dealing with a cost/benefit study, it is important to remember that there is one certain alternative to every decision we make, and that alternative is not to make any decision. In the case of Santa Barbara, not making a decision would have meant continuing to do what the nation was doing at the time. I believe that in 1969 we were not importing very much oil—let us suppose we were importing 35 percent of our oil—and the decision was either to go ahead with the Santa Barbara leasing or not to go ahead. The alternative we faced was another barrel of imported oil. There are external costs of imported oil, and if we are to consider the pros and cons of the Santa Barbara lease, we have to factor in the externalities from the alternative, which makes the analysis that much more complicated. I would like to emphasize this point.

It distresses me that we are spending so much money assessing the environmental impact of outer continental shelf development and so little money assessing the environmental impact of the alternatives. We do not have a substantial environmental study on the impact on the world's oceans of importing oil in tankers. We do not have environmental studies for the development of shale oil or coal in the midwestern or western states. If we are really going to make it national policy to try to quantify and evaluate these external costs, I think we should do it across the board (as much as we can), looking at all the alternatives.

If I may take another minute or so here, I would like to pick a few nits just as a professional. I was a little disturbed by the fact that Dr. Mead seemed to believe that the value of something should be based on its competitive price and that the monopoly price was irrelevant. It seems to me that if the OPEC cartel prevails and maintains oil at $11.00 a barrel, the fact that the competitive price of oil would be 15 cents or 25 cents or $1.50 or whatever would be simply irrelevant. The United States must make its decisions according to what oil costs us, and it will cost us $11.00 a barrel as long as OPEC maintains that price. If a marginal barrel is going to cost $11.00, the benefit of producing another barrel of domestic oil is also going to be $11.00. Clearly there is a slip in Dr. Mead's line of reasoning here. I would, however, agree that in doing cost/benefit studies, we should take as the costs of any project the real resource costs. But in the presence of a monopoly it is not clear that the monopoly price prevailing in the market is not in fact the proper measure of the benefit.

A second nit that I would like to pick has to do with internalizing oil-spill liability costs. Professor Mead believes they have been overinternalized, because the costs from lawsuits and some of the private costs that were compensated were not social costs. I think it is important to note that there is a major problem with delayed compensation. The courts have not yet grasped the notion of present value in compensation and typically provide compensation equivalent to the cost of something at the time of the incident. If it takes ten years to win a judgment for the money to repaint a boat, typically a court will only give enough money to cover the cost of painting the boat at the time it was damaged. The result is that the individual bears a substantial cost in the value of money forgone over the period of the suit. There is a need for some kind of liability repayment system that moves more quickly or at least that recognizes the time value of money.

I was a bit puzzled by the fact that in trying to differentiate between social costs and private costs, Professor Mead said that tourism was rather a peculiar externality since someone gained and someone lost, but that he seemed to believe commercial fishing losses were not so peculiar. I wonder about that: if the fishermen were not fishing they would have been engaged in some other activity. If, as Dr. Mead indicates, the fish catch stayed up, I am not clear it would be safe to include tourism and not fishing in that category of "peculiar externalities."

Robert Knecht

I would like to put the coastal zone management program in perspective, especially as it relates to offshore drilling. Now oil spills are important, obviously: we know what they are like; we have seen them in the past; and to a certain extent they are an emotional subject. But I think most of us believe the major impact of offshore drilling will be onshore, and I would therefore like to look more at the social cost of the major onshore effects of offshore drilling and less at the oil spill problem.

There are a number of conflicts in this area. The one I want to center on is the conflict between the federal government and the state governments over what course should be followed. As Professor Hargis pointed out, at the present time most of the coastal states in this country do not have the appropriate institutional mechanisms for dealing with the onshore effects. But there is hope; the states are working on these mechanisms. I want to give you a brief progress report.

While a lot of the North Sea experience is not transferable to this country and our OCS problems, some of it is. I think even the briefest visit to the North Sea is illuminating in providing examples of communities that are trying to plan in advance and to deal rationally with the problem—as, for example, the Shetland Islands. It is also illuminating in providing examples of communities that did not plan, and are suffering adverse economic, social, and other effects—as, for example, Aberdeen or Inverness or some of the smaller towns in that part of Scotland. I think there are lessons to be learned from the North Sea experience about the desirability of planning and getting the institutional mechanism in place, so that those affected feel they are a part of the process and are not being "done to," so to speak—that they are guiding the effects to a certain extent and minimizing or mitigating the adverse ones.

With that in mind, let us consider our own bright spot in building such institutions along the coastal zones of the United States. Congress passed the Coastal Zone Management Act in October 1972, a relatively unknown piece of legislation until quite recently. Under that act, federal aid has been made available to the coastal states first to develop and then to implement just the kinds of management programs and regulatory schemes that we are talking about, and to help resolve conflicts in the use of coastal resources—in particular, the use of coastal lands and water. It aims especially at those land-use decisions and commitments that have more than a local impact. It is encouraging to note that, while the program is a voluntary one, all the coastal states are now in it. Most of the states are just about to enter their second year of program funding. To date, about $9 million of federal money has been made available to the coastal states, and the coastal states have put up $4 or $5 million in matching funds. That makes a total program level of $13 or $14 million. All the states plan to have these programs developed and (they hope) implemented between June and September of 1977. This is not a long-term aesthetic program or an erudite planning program: its objective is to get a management program developed and in place—which means state legislation, regulation, and management.

The key question here is whether the states will stay in the program up to and including the implementation stage. It is one thing to apply for planning assistance and another to pass the kind of state legislation that may be required and that may affect state and local government relationships by transferring decision-making power from the local governments to the state capitol. To keep the states in the program is going to take real incentives for the state governments.

Since it is a voluntary program, there are two kinds of incentives: one is funding, and clearly that has to be there, but the second incentive is probably the more important one, that the states must be given a degree of leverage over federal actions. If the states develop these programs and have them approved at the federal level, federal licenses and permits must be consistent with state programs, and, in our interpretation, that would include giving the states leverage over leasing if they take the trouble to adopt programs that have the process-related requirements of the act built into them. This would be a valuable incentive, and I think the states are looking to see whether the federal government is taking this matter seriously. They are looking to see whether the federal government is prepared to respect state programs once they are developed and implemented, especially when it comes to issues like OCS development. I think the attention that has been focused on OCS development has served a valuable purpose in this sense: it has made clear to the coastal states the importance of getting on with the job of taking stock of their dealings with local governments, of coming up with the right kinds of regulatory schemes, and of getting them in place promptly.

I believe the coastal states will do a responsible job. They will develop and implement programs on a timely basis, and these programs will contain an adequate response on the siting of coastal facilities, provided four things happen: first, that the states have a greater voice than they have had so far in setting the standards of environmental information—the baseline programs—that should surround key federal decision making on offshore oil; second, that they have adequate funding for program development; third, that they be convinced that there will be a reconciliation between the plans that are approved by the Department of the Interior for developing an oil field and the state coastal zone programs—in other words, that the federal consistency provision in the act will be applied; and fourth, that they be compensated for any net adverse effects suffered in the siting of facilities required in the larger national interest.

So much for the brief overview of the program. What I would like to do now is comment on the application of the idea of social cost to the problem of the onshore impact of OCS development. Professor Mead applied it for the most part to the oil spill program, but I think the onshore impact of development is the major part of the problem. The difficulty here (as he noted) is that the benefits tend to be applied over a wide area—the whole nation—while the costs tend to be applied over a much narrower and localized area. Different sets of people tend to receive the benefits on the one hand and pay the costs on the other.

Even if the total social benefits in developing a particular offshore oil field could be shown to be much greater than the total social costs, we might have a hard time convincing the people of the town that is going to be directly involved in the siting of the refinery or the oil storage facilities that development is reasonable. Now in the Congress there are a number of pieces of legislation that attempt to deal with just this kind of problem. One measure, Senate Bill 586, would authorize a coastal impact fund to compensate states and localities for adverse effects that I would equate with Professor Mead's social costs. In effect, these funds would be obtained from those benefitting—that is to say, from the national treasury—and fed back to the local people paying the costs.

Let me mention five kinds of social costs that seem to be appropriate in considering onshore impact. First, there are the costs of planning for the regulation of onshore and near-shore oil-related facilities. These would involve listing resource areas that would not be appropriate for the siting of facilities, listing suitable sites, developing siting processes, and so on. Second, there are the costs of operating the regulatory program (call it coastal zone management), including a monitoring program to provide some sort of feedback to guarantee that the program is working. Third, there are the costs of the additional public facilities needed to ameliorate the adverse environmental impact of the oil-related facilities. These could include additions to local sewage treatment plants, buffer lands around energy facilities, and so on. Fourth, there are the costs of public acquisition of land to counterbalance coastal zone uses—for example, land for recreation and conservation. If, in the national interest, coastal states and communities are required to adopt processes to site energy-related facilities, then a similar requirement should exist for their acquiring coastal lands to counterbalance energy-related use of land. Certainly the coastal states are thinking along these lines. Fifth and last, there are the infrastructure costs—the costs of additional public facilities and services, from schools to police, needed to support the new population brought in by the oil industry. Eventually tax revenues generated by the facilities might well cover these costs or even exceed them, but there is nonetheless a timing question, what might be called a question of front-end costs.

Now, it is difficult to get a handle on the magnitude of these costs, and there is a wide range of opinion. As we learned earlier in this conference there is little agreement on the magnitude of the resources. There is little agreement on the additional facilities required onshore—any discussion between state people and industry people will reveal that instantly. For example, industry believes that a thousand acres will be needed for onshore facilities for the Baltimore Canyon. The Council on Environmental Quality reports suggest a figure tending more toward the tens of thousands of acres, perhaps approaching 50,000. I think the CEQ had a number like 90,000 acres devoted to onshore industry for the East Coast. Clearly there are great uncertainties here. At the National Oceanic and Atmospheric Administration we have been dealing with the coastal states on this problem. They are developing information now, and the range of annual social costs varies in their estimates from several million dollars per year up to $40 million per year for a heavily affected state.

One additional comment on assessing the costs of additional regulatory programs. Recently, the Office of Management and Budget has made it a requirement that inflationary impact statements be prepared for any new legislation or new regulations proposed by the administration. Calculations have to be carried out showing the additional costs of all kinds that would be incurred if the new regulations or legislation were to be adopted. This is an effort toward better understanding of the inflationary effects of any action and I think it is related to Professor Mead's suggestion about analyzing the costs and benefits of government regulations.

Let me summarize by saying we clearly have to pay attention to the correspondence—or the lack of correspondence—between the population receiving the benefits and the population paying the costs, and the difference between the timing of the payments and the timing of the benefits. Otherwise, we will have an unrealistic view of the problem.

Walter Mead

Both Mr. Cahill and Dr. Gaskins raised the question of the coastal state veto. Do the coastal states have the right to hold things up and say they are doing it because everyone is concerned? As long as the coastal states, whether California or the New England states, receive no share of the bonus payments for federal leases, no part of the royalty, no part of the rent—zero benefits from those three sources—and still bear the heavy potential costs of any oil spill, there will be local opposition to offshore federal leasing. Texas and Louisiana may be exceptions. But southern Californians and New Englanders are going to be opposed to federal oil leasing as long as they receive none of the proceeds.

If we want to get Pacific and Atlantic leasing under way agreeably rather than shoving it down the throats of the natives, it would be better to do what was suggested earlier by Professor Devanney, and divide up the pie a bit differently. If we take some of the benefits and distribute them locally, some of the local opposition will disappear. It has been suggested that we compensate local communities in case of a spill, but that will not really change the minds of the community, because the best that could happen is that the local community would break even.

Take Santa Barbara community for example. If we ask a hundred citizens in the street, "Do you want oil exploration and production out there?", we will get ninety-nine "no's" and the one who says "yes" will be employed by the oil industry. No one else is going to want development and there is no reason he should. The people of Santa Barbara bear the costs while the benefits accrue to the nation as a whole. I think one of Senator Henry Jackson's bills provides for redistributing benefits, which is important.

Darius Gaskins brought up the question of competition, and this morning Professor Devanney suggested that competition was not working on offshore leasing. Some time ago I did a study of competition in offshore leasing in which I asked if there were any evidence of monopoly in the early (1954–1955) OCS leases in the Gulf of Mexico. What I did was to calculate the companies' bonus payments, rental payments, and royalty payments, and estimate the exploration cost, production cost, and lifting cost. Exact data were available on oil production and gas production for 1954 through 1967, the terminal point in the study. I projected income and expenditures for the remaining life of the fields and calculated the internal rate of return.

If there were a monopoly and if the government were not getting its full income, then one would expect to find a rate of return to the oil companies in excess of normal, let us say in excess of 12 percent. The calculations yielded a before-tax rate of return of 7.5 percent, which is below normal. This tells us that the oil companies bid too much for those leases and that the federal government has obtained more than a fair price for them. There were about 200 leases in the study. It was not a small sample. It indicates that competition is working quite well indeed.

Since 1954–1955, the average number of bidders per sale has been increasing. The average number of bidders per tract sold has gone up by about 50 percent.

An increasing number of firms are successful bidders. Through 1974 there have been 132 firms winning federal offshore oil and gas leases. Vast increases in the average bid per acre occurred long before the recent crude oil price increases. The average bid per acre for 1954–1955 lease sales was $340, but for 1970–1972 sales the average was $2,252, a better than sixfold increase. If the 1954–1955 leases were competitive, then the more recent ones were probably even more so.

Darius Gaskins raised a question about the appropriate price of crude oil—$7.00 or $11.00 per barrel. The price one should use in analyzing a problem depends on the nature of the problem. If one is concerned about the long-run value of oil, then the present world price, which reflects the present monopoly power of OPEC, may give an imperfect signal. In my opinion, the power of OPEC is transitory and the price of oil will fall to around $7.00 by 1979 or 1980. If one is analyzing a long-term supply problem, $7.00 would be a better indication of the social value of oil than the present monopoly price. On the other hand, analysis of a short-term problem would require use of the present market price.

I should also point out, in defense of my distinguishing between tourism and fishing in the category of "peculiar externalities," that we netted out the fishermen who found other employment.

DISCUSSION

MR. SAVIT: The discussion by Professor Mead brought to mind a television news program I saw this morning. In this program there was considerable discussion of the plight of a large group of low-income families who face a substantial increase in their utility bills. It occurs to me that the increase in the utility bills is an internal cost being borne by these people. It represents, primarily, the difference between the $7.00 competitive cost of oil, its social cost, and the $11.00 monopoly price that exists today. This particular cost, then, is one factor that could be eliminated by developing offshore oil. There may be other costs, but no one seems to be addressing this particular cost.

Just what does it cost to wait and who does pay for the waiting while we determine whether we shall operate offshore, to what extent we shall operate, under what conditions, and under what controls? So far we have made a de facto decision to wait for development until we can settle our internal squabbles. Someone is paying, and it appears to me that the people who are paying the largest proportion of their personal income for this delay are the people in the low-income brackets, to whom fuel represents a larger proportion of their expenditures per month than it does to those in the higher-income brackets. It seems to me that concern about the detailed ecological impact on the life of birds which cannot reasonably be valued even at $10.00 is a concern for those upper-income people who are able to afford the luxury of dealing with the environment, as opposed to the lower-income people who simply want to keep their homes warm and get to work. Would Professor Mead comment?

PROFESSOR MEAD: Yes. There are two issues involved, an income distribution issue and a resource allocation issue. Darius Gaskins pointed out this distinction. It is true that the longer we delay introducing additional oil supplies into the market, the longer the price of oil supplies will remain high. At high prices, more wealth is transferred from consumers to producers. Restraints on new production prevent resources from flowing into such areas as offshore oil. This is a resource allocation matter.

MR. MEEKER: Both Professor Mead and Mr. Knecht talked about the relationship of the coastal states to the nation: there are obviously a number of ways of dealing with that relationship. As I understood Mr. Knecht's presentation, he would not limit the compensation to states to the estimated social cost of an oil spill, but would have the nation as a whole, through the federal government, reimburse the states for their net losses from the onshore impact of OCS development. This would seem to be a sound approach. Indeed I think this approach would be fairer overall than any of the plans reflected in several bills that have been before Congress that would simply allocate a percentage of OCS federal revenues to the coastal states. To do that, without relating the revenues allocated to the impact on the particular coastal states, would be arbitrary. That impact should be estimated as carefully and as fairly as possible, and then the nation—which is receiving the benefits—should defray the expense an individual coastal state is sustaining.

PROFESSOR MEAD: This is primarily an income distribution matter. If we want to shift income from the federal government—which is all of the people—to the people of Santa Barbara who suffered from the spill, we are simply redistributing income. That may be a proper thing to do, but it will not affect the decision of people in the New England states to support oil development off New England. If our objective is to affect the decision of the people of New England, we will have to redistribute the pie, not only in the sense of paying off the losses, but in the sense of overcoming the resistance to offshore oil activity in New England coastal communities.

MR. SARGUIS: I wonder if Professor Mead, when he set up his social benefit/cost analysis, considered the fact that the spill from Platform A has never been fully controlled and still continues. I also wonder if he has taken into account the fact that the containment and recovery techniques employed in 1969 were less than fully adequate, less than 100 percent effective, and have therefore left behind a residue of damage. Our beaches in Santa Barbara still get oil, and we have statements from many long-time Santa Barbara residents that attribute the beach goo to the oil activities in the channel. I am wondering why the social cost analysis did not take into account the loss of tax revenues to the city of Santa Barbara proper. Professor Mead indicated that the motel trade went on down or up the coast, but that might have been outside Santa Barbara.

PROFESSOR MEAD: It might have been, but it was not. Goleta expanded its bed tax revenue rapidly, and Montecito—

MR. SARGUIS: The point is they are not in the city of Santa Barbara; they are in the county.

PROFESSOR MEAD: In any case, it is nothing but a transfer; it is not a social cost.

MR. SARGUIS: There are taxpayers in the city who pay a tax, which is uniquely a city tax.

PROFESSOR MEAD: But the taxes were paid elsewhere. The loss of city taxes is not a social cost, it is only a transfer: Santa Barbara's loss was someone else's gain. I was after the social cost, not the transfers.

MR. SARGUIS: What is the framework of the society you are projecting? Is it countywide, statewide, national?

PROFESSOR MEAD: The frame of reference was national. Your other question concerned continued leakage. We used a generally accepted figure of about 3.3 million gallons. There has been a little bit of spillage beyond that since 1969. I doubt very much if it would cause the 3.3 million gallon estimate to change significantly. The collection efforts are still imperfect, and this is a beautiful example of social waste. I understand that Union Oil, as the operator, has placed ten collecting tents below the surface of the water. Those ten collecting tents are collecting approximately one barrel of oil per day. That is a terrible social waste. The cost of avoiding spillage of one barrel per day must exceed the social cost of such spillage by an order of magnitude.

MR. SARGUIS: I wonder if I can finish. I should indicate, while we are talking about social waste, that straw was the most effective method of cleaning the beaches in 1969 and technological developments have been such that today straw remains the most effective way to clean the beaches after an oil spill. But I would like to ask Dr. Mead what social cost or value he places on the fact that a very large segment of the population in Santa Barbara paid premium prices to come there, either by way of giving up high-paying jobs or by way of paying more for property because of the uniqueness of the community, and then had a major spill occur which obviously left a serious mark on the entire community?

PROFESSOR MEAD: We did our best to measure that social cost. We tried to count it as part of the recreational loss, but I do not think we got it all. We also had a loss in value of real estate. We measured that one, again, very imperfectly.

WILLIAM REILLY, The Conservation Foundation: I would like to ask a dumb, but not facetious, question. I have the impression that one reason a good many people are excited about this debate, or worried about offshore drilling, is because they saw pictures of the birds that were affected by oil in the Santa Barbara spill. What value would one put on those birds? Is there a way to factor in the effect their destruction had on so many people?

PROFESSOR MEAD: I do not know how we could get at it. Certainly it has been a major element in the thinking of many people: that *Life* magazine article had a terrific impact on the nation. Those poor struggling birds tore the reader's heart out, but nevertheless that was primarily an emotional issue. We know we lost many birds, but at the moment we have no satisfactory way to put a value on them. The thing we must recognize about that Santa Barbara oil spill is that it was a terrible insult. Looking at that blackened beach in 1969 was a sickening experience. We tried to capture that in the recreational study, and we got some pretty high values from some of the people interviewed.

PROFESSOR DORFMAN: My question is pretty much along those same lines, having to do with the $16.5 million or $16.4 million social cost. That kind of analysis makes me uncomfortable. Let me express my discomfort in two ways. First, according to the table, most of the detectable social costs could have been avoided simply by not bothering to clean up the mess, since that is how they were incurred, but I think something must be wrong with that; second, and I think this echoes what Mr. Reilly was just saying, if we were to imagine that a dragon were to appear off the coast of Santa Barbara now and then and that, unless he were paid an x-million-dollar ransom, he would spit out 3 million gallons of oil (as dragons are known to have done), I think we would be willing to pay that ransom, even if x were a lot more than $16 million. By coming up with a hard figure like that, we come away believing that is all there is, or at least that is most of what there is. Except before a sophisticated audience, I think that could be a very dangerous kind of figure to perpetrate.

CAPTAIN COUSTEAU: I would like to limit my remarks to this paper, though I have a lot of other remarks that I have so far had no time to express. To my knowledge, and perhaps I am wrong, the only oil spill that was scientifically well documented was the spill by Woods Hole on the East Coast. That oil spill was much smaller than the Santa Barbara spill, but from a biological standpoint it was a disaster and it still is a disaster. I do not know how well the biological consequences of the Santa Barbara oil spill are being studied now and how they can be compared with the background data that exist, but I am very much disturbed that there is such a discrepancy between the results at Woods Hole and the optimistic expression of the results at Santa Barbara.

The second thing I would like to touch on is tourism. I think it is difficult to assess what the tourists suffered, because, in fact, quite a few people went to Santa Barbara to see the oil spill. There is a kind of an attraction to a disaster. Every time there is a disaster, people go to look at the dead and the spilled blood. I know my people went there to have Senator Tunney dive under the oil spill and see for himself, and so, of course, we rented rooms there, though we were not exactly tourists. This economic cost and benefit analysis has to be made, of course, but it seems to me there are serious doubts about everything apart from the cost of cleaning the beaches. That was presumably easy to develop.

Now on the value of birds, which is "emotional." I disagree. It is not so emotional as Professor Mead seems to think. We Europeans suffered during the war; our country was plundered by the enemy and many people were killed. When peace came, we were all asked to fill in forms to tell what damage we had suffered, and in ten years, if you had a house that had been damaged, you were reimbursed. All the material damage was reimbursed, just as the cleaning of the beach at Santa Barbara was paid for by the oil companies. But for the children of my friends who had been killed during the war, there was no compensation, because no one can put a value on life. What is the value of the moose that will disappear as a result of the Alaskan pipeline? What is the value of the fact, not that a bird is killed but that if a species of bird is eliminated, our children and grandchildren and hundreds of generations (if there are hundreds of generations) will be deprived of the joy of seeing that kind of bird. This is something that completely escapes benefit/cost analysis.

PROFESSOR MEAD: On Professor Dorfman's point, the problem we were concerned with here was the cost of the Santa Barbara oil spill and of what happened there. In fact, the beach was cleaned up. That required the use of labor, machinery, gasoline, and so forth. We evaluated what in fact was done. It would do no good to say we might have stopped doing it because we were not asking what should have been done. We were asking about the cost of what happened, and the cleanup efforts did in fact happen. Of course, a lot of silly things also happened. The cleanup crews did in fact spread straw, and then they picked up the straw which had oil attached to it, transported it, and spilled it up in the canyons. This is still a spill, but in a less obvious location. Part of the cleanup benefit was not cost-justified. On the other hand, if no cleanup effort had been made, then there would have been additional recreational and presumably other social costs.

I cannot say much about the East Coast comparison, except that there were different circumstances. We tried to evaluate the Santa Barbara spill only. As to what happens if a species of bird is eliminated, I can only say I do not know. Happily, we did not have to deal with that question, because no elimination of species occurred in the Santa Barbara case. In any case, an economist must take the input of the biologists, because he is not a biologist. Our methodology represents a beginning: it is weak, and it has all kinds of problems. We asked the biologists questions, and they gave us the answers from speculation and from what research they have done. Baseline work was inadequate before this spill. I recently asked biologists at the University of California, Santa Barbara, if there were now any evidence that there was a spill. Is there any spill evidence on bird life today? They said they could not see any. Bird life is the same as it was before the spill, so far as they know. Happily, we did not have to deal with the question of elimination of a species.

CAPTAIN COUSTEAU: I believe I agree, but my question was how it would be evaluated.

PROFESSOR MEAD: I think I would work on another problem at that point.

MR. KNECHT: Professor Mead may have netted the fishermen, which is rather the reverse of the usual procedure, but at least his paper was not for the birds.

PART FOUR

The Appropriate Pace of Offshore Drilling

Irvin White opened the final panel of the day, warning of a developing confrontation between the federal government, bent on accelerating offshore development, and the coastal states, some of which believe development is being rushed. Professor White pointed to various restraints that will slow the rate of development, these ranging from a shortage of mobile drilling rigs to inadequate government managerial capacity, but he emphasized that the pace will essentially be determined by the accommodation worked out between the federal government and the other interested parties. His remarks produced several expressions of opposition to the accelerated development program, including a warning that because of a shortage of experienced engineers, such an effort would increase the threat of another oil spill of the Santa Barbara variety. Professor White's words also touched off a controversy over proposals to separate exploration and production into distinct phases, advocates of planning contending with advocates of prompt action. And there was further argument whether the OPEC cartel will endure and what will happen to the price of oil.

THE APPROPRIATE PACE OF OFFSHORE DRILLING

Irvin L. White

As a starting point, I would like to use Mr. Solomon's division of the analyses to be undertaken in evaluating offshore oil and gas development into legal analysis and scientific analysis. And I would like to disagree, or at least to suggest that a third kind—political analysis—would have an overriding importance. The true topic for this session of the conference is what happens when we get down to making political accommodations. I have been asked to speak on the appropriate pace of offshore drilling, but I would like to broaden the question a little. I think the broader form is probably implicit in the way the question was stated initially, but whether it is or not, I have purposely addressed the more general question, "What is the appropriate pace for developing offshore oil and gas resources?" The change permits me to view drilling as but one of the technological and social activities involved in developing these offshore resources, and permits me also to direct attention to significant problems that must be resolved if we are to decide the appropriate pace for developing these resources.

I believe that, if properly conducted, increased offshore production is generally the most attractive short-to-middle-term option available for significantly increasing domestic production of liquid and gaseous fuels. Some of my colleagues in the Science and Public Policy Program at the University of Oklahoma may not agree with me: in fact, I would be surprised if all of them do agree. Nevertheless, for several reasons I take the position that offshore development is an attractive alternative. These reasons include the quantity of oil and gas resources located offshore, the broad range of substitution options that oil and gas offer, and the fact that outer continental shelf development seems generally to pose fewer environmental threats than does the development of almost any other domestic energy source. I intend to discuss each of these points briefly, together with some of the constraints, problems, and issues that are likely to determine what the actual pace of offshore development will be. These include such considerations as (1) the availability of capital, manpower, materials, and equipment; (2) the need to enhance government capabilities for managing offshore resource development; and (3) what now appears to be a rapidly developing confrontation between the federal government and many of the coastal states adjacent to frontier areas of the outer continental shelf.

Table 1
ESTIMATES OF UNDISCOVERED RECOVERABLE U.S. OIL RESOURCES
(billions of barrels)

Source	Onshore	Offshore	Total
National Petroleum Council (1972)	90	64	154
Mobil Oil (1974)	34	54	88
National Academy of Sciences (1975)	—	—	113
Hubbert (1974)	27	45	72
U.S. Geological Survey	136–272	64–128	200–400

Source: U.S. Congress, Senate, Committee on Commerce, National Ocean Policy Study, *An Analysis of the Department of the Interior's Accelerated Development of Oil and Gas on the Outer Continental Shelf,* March 1975.

Let me begin by elaborating my reasons for concluding that, if properly conducted, increased offshore production is generally the most attractive short-to-middle-term option available for increasing domestic production of liquid and gaseous fuels. As I noted, large quantities of oil and gas are believed to be located offshore. Just how much is, as we all know, a matter of considerable controversy. Table 1 shows the range of estimates for the OCS, from the low of King Hubbert's 45 billion barrels to the U.S. Geological Survey's 64 to 128 billion barrels. Regardless of which estimate is taken, most of the estimators agree that a large portion of the remaining discoverable energy resources in the United States will be found offshore and in Alaska, and specifically, that 30 to 35 percent of what is to be found will be found on the OCS.

This leads me to my second reason for concluding that offshore development is an attractive alternative—the substitutability of offshore oil and gas for oil and gas currently used. When we talk about the quantity of resources available, we should recall that our short-to-middle-range options are pretty much limited to fossil fuels, and among these fossil fuels, only oil and natural gas occur naturally as liquids and gases, the fuel forms that have shaped energy infrastructure development in the United States. Not only is most of the energy we consume in liquids or gases, but the major part of our energy distribution system is designed to accommodate these forms of energy.

As for consumption, Table 2 shows that the United States consumed almost 70,000 trillion Btus in 1971. This energy was used in four broad consuming sectors—residential and commercial, industrial, transportation, and electrical generation. The first three—residential and commercial, industrial, and transportation—accounted for 21 percent, 29 percent, and 25 percent of domestic energy consumption, respectively. Petroleum and natural gas comprised approximately two-thirds of the total resource input to these sectors. Most of the liquids and gases were used to accommodate space heating and cooling of buildings, trans-

96

Table 2

U.S. CONSUMPTION OF ENERGY BY MAJOR SOURCES AND CONSUMING SECTORS, 1971

Consumption Sector	Energy Source (trillion Btus)					Total Sector Input	Percent of National Total
	Coal [a]	Petroleum [b]	Natural gas	Nuclear power	Hydro-power		
Residential and commercial	390	6,545	7,346	—	—	14,281	20.7
Industrial	4,465	5,391	10,438	—	—	20,294	29.4
Transportation	7	16,139	825	—	—	16,971	24.6
Electrical generation	7,698	2,417	4,125	405	2,798	17,443	25.3
Total	12,560	30,492	22,734	405	2,798	68,989	100.0
Percent of national total	18.2	44.2	33.0	0.5	4.1		

[a] Includes anthracite, bituminous, and lignite.

[b] Petroleum products refined and processed from crude oil, including still gas, liquefied gas, and natural gas liquids.

Source: Adapted from U.S. Department of the Interior, *United States Energy through the Year 2000* (Washington, D. C.: Government Printing Office, 1972).

portation fuel needs, and industrial heat-process requirements. In fact, transportation currently accounts for more than half the U.S. petroleum consumption and has continued to increase its share. Likewise, industry uses about half of the natural gas demanded by these three sectors. If we add to these figures the amount of oil and gas used to generate electricity, we find that liquids and gases accounted for more than 75 percent of our domestic energy consumption in 1971. It must now be obvious that ours is a society predominantly dependent upon liquid and gaseous fuels.

If we are going to switch our dependence to solid fossil fuel resources like coal and oil shale, resources that we possess in large quantities domestically, either we will have to carry out substantial reconstruction of our energy infrastructure—something we are unlikely, or probably unable, to do over a short time—or else the solid resources will have to be converted into liquids or gases. Of course, coal as a solid fuel could be substituted for the oil and gas now being consumed by electric utilities and some industrial users, but this substitution would tend to exchange a supply problem for an environmental problem. I said earlier that one of the reasons offshore development is appealing is that it appears generally to be less environmentally threatening than most energy alternatives. This certainly seems to be the case when offshore development as a general category is compared to the extraction and conversion of coal and oil shale, our two most likely middle-term alternative sources of liquid and gaseous fuels.

The environmental threat of various energy alternatives can be compared in a number of different ways. We at the Science and Public Policy Program of the University of Oklahoma recently completed a study on this topic for an interagency committee of the federal government. In our report, entitled *Energy Alternatives: A Comparative Analysis*, we describe eleven energy resource systems. Each of these eleven descriptions identifies, to the extent now possible, the residuals or by-products that will be produced along with the primary energy products. These residuals are what produce the environmental impact, and it is possible to compare energy alternatives on the basis of the residuals they produce.

Without going into the details of this system of analysis, I have included in Table 3 some of the air- and water-pollutant residuals that will be produced by the development of offshore oil as compared to those that will be produced by the liquefaction of coal. Coal liquefaction using the consol synthetic fuel (CSF) process is expected to produce more than twenty times the quantity of water pollutants and more than eleven times the quantity of air pollutants that offshore oil production will produce. The only offshore residuals in this comparison that would be larger than those for coal liquefaction are organics and biochemical oxygen demand (BOD) and chemical oxygen demand (COD). Of course, this says nothing about either the water that will be demanded for most of the coal conversion processes or the enormous land reclamation problems that will have to be resolved.

98

Table 3

A COMPARISON OF SELECTED ENERGY ALTERNATIVES

(4.3×10^{15} Btus per year or 2.1 million barrels of oil per day)

Pollutants (tons per year)	Offshore Oil	Coal Liquefaction (CSF)
Water		
Bases	0	5,720
Dissolved solids	0	378,000
Suspended solids	0	1,980
Organics	18,800	10
Other	380	0
Total	19,200	386,000
Air (tons per year)		
Particulates	740	127,000
NO_x	21,000	424,000
SO_x	1,540	101,000
Hydrocarbons	25,700	19,600
CO	12,800	45,900
Aldehydes, etc.	340	5,180
Total	62,100	723,000

Source: Council on Environmental Quality, *Matrix of Environmental Residuals for Energy Systems* (Hittman Associates, 1974 and 1975). Science and Public Policy Program, University of Oklahoma, *Energy Alternatives: A Comparative Analysis* (Washington, D. C.: Government Printing Office, 1975).

I want to emphasize, however, that environmental analysis is incomplete if it stops at this point, since the residuals that will produce environmental effects have not been related to the conditions at the places those effects will occur. In other words, what I have just summarized for you in comparing offshore development with coal liquefaction stops short of comparing either potential or actual effects. That is why I have been careful to say that, if properly conducted, increased offshore production is generally the most attractive short-to-middle-term option available for increasing domestic energy production. I have not said, nor would it be reasonable to say, that all offshore development is more attractive than all other energy options. There may well be areas where local conditions make offshore development undesirable, or at least less desirable than coal conversion. There are sites where the residuals from offshore oil and gas development may pose unacceptable environmental risks. That is why the environmental impact statement process is so important. In environmental analysis, the residuals produced by the required technological activities are related to site-specific environmental conditions. Only when that has been done are we in a position to make judgments about specific developments at particular locations.

99

In order to avoid being misunderstood, I wish to make one additional point about environmental analysis. As many of you know, at the Science and Public Policy Program of the University of Oklahoma, we have consistently maintained that incomplete knowledge is not, ipso facto, justification for no action or no development. It might be if we lived in an ideal world, but we must be quite aware that we do not. We constantly must deal with uncertainty, and we must balance benefits and costs on a daily basis without being able to predict the outcomes or effects of our acts or choices with any real degree of confidence. The most reasonable way to deal with these limitations is to establish and nurture a management-planning system capable of responsive, sensitive, flexible management of resource development and capable of facilitating the achievement of political accommodations among the major competing interests.

Now I wish to carry on a brief discussion of some of the constraints, problems, and issues that are likely to determine what the actual pace of offshore development will be. At the outset, I must say that, for the immediate future, I cannot imagine many things likely to slow development more than some of the actions being taken by administration officials. I refer to the administration's insistence on accelerating the oil leasing program for the OCS to the point of planning to lease 10 million acres in 1975 and the recent premature call for nominations of tracts to be leased in the Baltimore Canyon area. I refer to Federal Energy Administrator Zarb's reported insistence on an energy facilities planning and development bill that would give the federal government an override or preemptive role in siting energy facilities. Most of the constraints, problems, and issues that are the subject of our discussion today are either caused, exacerbated, or otherwise affected by such actions and policies.

One set of factors that must be considered in determining the appropriate rate for developing offshore resources is the availability of capital, materials, equipment, and personnel. First of all, it should be emphasized that accelerated offshore development cannot be considered apart from our total energy development program. In its 1970 report, *U.S. Energy Prospects: An Engineering Viewpoint*, the Task Force on Energy of the National Academy of Engineering concluded that any major program on the scale required to approach energy self-sufficiency might well be seriously restrained by capital requirements. The task force estimated a need for more than $500 billion to $600 billion and for substantially more specialized manpower. Some of the estimates in the report are staggering. To develop coal resources at the suggested rate would require, among other items, 125,000 new coal miners, 2,000 mechanized longwall mining machines, 50 new 200-cubic-yard shovels, 4,000 new locomotives, 100,000 one-hundred-ton-capacity gondola cars, 20 new 2-million-ton barge systems, 10 new 25-million-ton-per-year slurry pipelines, and so on. Add to this the additional requirements for crude oil and natural gas development at an accelerated rate and for developing oil shale, nuclear fusion and other sources of energy—but presumably I have made my point.

Let us focus on a specific restraint that affects the Department of the Interior's accelerated OCS development program—the availability of mobile drilling rigs. As I mentioned earlier, the department's program calls for leasing 10 million acres in 1975. There is good reason to doubt the ability of the petroleum industry to explore this much new acreage within the five years allowed by the terms of current OCS lease agreements. Studies by the Federal Energy Administration and National Petroleum Council and two recent congressional studies conclude that mobile drilling rigs are likely to be a constraint on offshore oil and gas development, both because of the small number of rigs currently available and because of the lack of worldwide capacity for building new ones. A recent study by the National Science Foundation's National Ocean Policy Study staff concluded that by 1980 there would be a total of 148 rigs in U.S. waters capable of drilling in water depths of more than 100 feet. This estimate may be conservative, since it does not assume that rigs currently outside U.S. waters would be attracted back to the United States by the accelerated leasing program. In fact, the Department of the Interior expects quite a contrary result. However, it should be noted that the department's environmental impact statement for the Mississippi, Alabama, and Florida lease sale in December 1973 predicted that twenty-six rigs would be exploring the leased area by the end of 1974. Actually, only six rigs were exploring in this area by January 1975. I recognize, of course, this is a relatively short term against which to judge long-term rig availability. However, in a recent survey of future rig availability, *Offshore: The Journal of Ocean Business* predicted that overall rig demand would be well beyond shipyard capacity worldwide through at least 1982. Altogether, it seems reasonable to conclude that rig availability may well act as a significant restraint on accelerated OCS development, and this should be taken into account in our overall energy planning.

Let us turn now to management as a constraint. An evaluation of the federal government's demonstrated capability to manage OCS development does not clearly establish the government's ability to cope with an accelerated rate of development. The present system has many management problems, primarily because of a lack of personnel, inadequate in-house expertise, and a lack of sufficient data. The present leasing system provides for the sale of leases before the presence of recoverable reserves is actually established. Both government and industry have to make leasing decisions without this information, but government managers in the Bureau of Land Management and the U.S. Geological Survey are clearly at a decided disadvantage. In a recent study of accelerated OCS development, an ad hoc committee of the House Committee on Banking and Currency concluded that the U.S. Geological Survey has not been adequately staffed to permit it to make accurate estimates of the value of the offshore resources that the Bureau of Land Management has been selling.

Because of inadequate staffing, generally poor geologic information, and the engineering criteria upon which its estimates have been based, the Geological

Survey's estimates have generally been conservative. But published evaluations may be somewhat misleading since they compare Geological Survey estimates to the high rather than the median or average bid. In fact, the survey's record has improved considerably since it began using a range-of-values model. Nonetheless, fair value return to the public is a highly visible and significantly public policy issue at the present time. Accelerated leasing decisions should take this fact into account, and the acceleration rate should be matched to the capabilities of the Bureau of Land Management and the U.S. Geological Survey to manage the increase.

This is particularly the case when we come to questions that have been raised concerning wells completed and shut in. In testimony before the Subcommittee on Activities of Regulatory Agencies of the House Permanent Select Committee on Small Business, a Department of the Interior spokesman indicated that, contrary to Outer Continental Shelf Order No. 5, shut-in wells are not verified to determine that they are, in fact, shut in for a legitimate purpose—as, for example, to correct a production problem such as low pressure. The same hearings also illuminated an interesting case of two Gulf of Mexico tracts located six miles apart. A twenty-eight-mile pipeline was built to permit production of natural gas on one of the tracts, but wells drilled on the tract six miles away where shut in, although reportedly that tract contained twice the amount of gas discovered on the tract being produced. Now there may be some explanation for this apparent discrepancy, but, even if there is, it did not come out at the hearings.

This kind of thing will continue to contribute to public distrust until the public can be assured it is not being bilked either by a greedy industry or by inadequate government management. At least for the short term, the public will have to be shown that the government manager is protecting the public interest. This is going to mean the public will have to provide more adequate resources to the government manager, and that is likely to slow the rate at which OCS development can be accelerated.

I believe that the problems I have discussed up to this point are important and that they will tend to slow the rate at which OCS resources will be developed. But these problems are not nearly so significant potentially as the confrontation that seems to be developing between the federal and coastal state governments, a problem discussed earlier by Mr. Knecht. It is fair to say that the public record demonstrates a high degree of insensitivity on the part of some federal agencies to the legitimate concerns of the coastal states, particularly those states adjacent to frontier areas that would be affected by the Department of the Interior's accelerated OCS development program. This is not to say that all the states have acted in good faith. It is possible that at least some of the states are motivated by greed or are determined to use every available tactic to delay development as long as possible. Whatever their reasons, the states seem to be reaching a consensus, and they and their congressional delegations seem determined to bring about some basic changes in the present system for developing OCS resources.

One of their major goals is to change the system so that separate decisions are required for exploring and for developing OCS resources. In addition, the states want financial assistance from the federal government to help pay for the planning required to mitigate onshore effects as well as to help pay the cost of providing the public facilities and public services required to support offshore development. Separating exploration and development into two phases is intended to provide the states with more adequate information than they have about resources and thereby to lessen the uncertainty they must deal with in their planning. It is also intended to provide the federal government with sufficient information to create a phased and measured OCS development program as a part of an integrated overall national energy plan.

Justifiably or not, several of the coastal states believe OCS development is being rushed. They argue that the Department of the Interior should at least delay accelerated development until the coastal states have completed the coastal zone management plans encouraged by federal legislation enacted in 1972. The debate is being framed in terms of states' rights against the broader national interest, in terms of the environmental risks of OCS development and in terms of the social, economic and aesthetic onshore consequences that will flow from offshore development.

What is needed here is enlightened and reasoned debate, not confrontation. Energy is so fundamental a need in our technological society that all our fossil fuel energy resources will have to be developed either as fuels or as feedstocks. Our energies would be much better spent devising the least environmentally threatening development technologies and the most equitable social strategies than in confrontation. As a reading of energy bills introduced into the current session of Congress will reveal, the debate is about to begin in earnest. The actual pace of offshore development will depend largely on the outcome of the debate centered around these bills and the opposing approaches they propose.

At the outset I said that I intended to address the question, "What is the appropriate pace for developing our offshore oil and gas resources?" Being true to my profession, I have answered that question by indirection. I said why I believe that, if properly conducted, increased offshore production is generally the most attractive short-to-middle-term option available for increasing domestic energy production. I also said that there are a number of restraints that in the end will probably determine what the actual rate will be. I also said that I do not believe OCS development should be forced upon the coastal states. These states should not be required to bear a disproportionate share of the social and environmental costs of development, certainly not unless they are involved in planning a phased and measured development program and compensated in some way for the risks and costs they will bear for the rest of us.

Having said all this indirectly, I can conclude directly that the appropriate rate of offshore development is one that can be supported by the best available technologies, carried out by the most highly qualified operators, overseen by a competent government manager with adequate staff, and conducted under a plan which takes into account significant site-specific differences and the legitimate concerns of the adjacent coastal states, as well as the energy needs of the entire nation. In the long term, only such a rate will serve the national interest no matter how we choose individually to define it.

COMMENTARY AND RESPONSE

J. R. Jackson, Jr.

I feel, as a representative of a major oil company, that I have been given a pretty thorough beating today. I would like to try to respond to some of the comments that have been made. I am particularly happy that Governor Byrne of New Jersey has come in, because he is responsible for some of the points I want to speak to, and I want him to hear my comments. I would like to suggest, first, that those who are interested in the profitability of major oil companies should take a look at the Senate Finance Committee report dated 1974 (93rd Congress, 2d session). There is a great deal of significant information there: the report gives rates of foreign and domestic net income and the taxes paid by the major oil companies. I think this might set to rest some of the apprehensions that have been voiced today.

The appropriate rate of offshore oil and gas development must be considered in the perspective of our current and future energy picture and our growing dependence on foreign imports. It must also be considered in the light or darkness of a national energy policy long awaited, much discussed, and now bogged down in the miasma of politics, while the essential scientific and technical details are ignored. I think this context is highly relevant to some of the comments being made by those who do not have the appropriate knowledge, the appropriate scientific and technical information, to make them.

I generally agree with Professor White's opening statement that, properly conducted, increased offshore production is the most attractive—indeed the only—medium-term solution for increasing our domestic self-sufficiency in fuels. Let me add that it is also the only short-term solution for greater conservation, if assisted by increasing imports. Professor White has chosen to address the assigned subject somewhat obliquely by discussing some real problems and some non-problems that could become real problems if the Congress and the administration act in irresponsible ways, or if they elect to pay heed to those who would stop all forms of domestic energy development. Let me speak directly to the subject he addressed obliquely.

Domestic oil and gas production in the United States has peaked and is declining, and, at best, we hope the rate of decline can be arrested. We have drilled over 1.3 million wells in the United States, the most attractive onshore areas have been thoroughly explored, the great Gulf of Mexico offshore has peaked, and its oil production is declining. There is little chance left for large wildcat (or any other) oil discoveries, either onshore or in the mature areas offshore. This is not to say that we will not find a few large fields and a number of small fields, or that we will not continue to increase our percentage of recovery from those reserves that are known today, albeit at a gradual rate: we do have secondary recovery methods. Indeed, there is a great deal of secondary recovery going on. A great part of our production today comes from secondary and tertiary recovery. Water flooding has been going on for twenty or thirty years. But gains from secondary or tertiary recovery come at a very slow rate, and we are not going to increase our percentages of recovery dramatically. I think we should realize that these increases are going to be at the rate of a quarter of 1 percent or a half of 1 percent per year.

The best future available finds are offshore and in the onshore basin within the interior of Alaska. Petroleum will be the dominant energy source for many years and must serve as the bridge to those future sources of unlimited, non-polluting, and (one hopes) cheap energy. These future sources are several decades in the future. I strongly oppose attempts to separate exploration and production operations. The separation would create unnecessary delays, is ill-advised, technically unsound, naive, and displays a lack of knowledge of geology and the exploration process. It would trade industry knowledge for risk, red tape, and politics. That trade would be unnecessary for environmental assistance and contrary to public policy and the national interest.

I generally agree with Professor White in his judgment that the appropriate rate for oil and gas development is the best accelerated rate that can be supported by the free enterprise private oil and gas industry, using the latest and best technology, carried out by highly qualified operators under federal regulations, administered by an appropriate and competent governmental agency, and taking into account the legitimate concerns of the affected coastal states. Adequate compensation should of course be provided for any undue environmental or economic effects on those states.

Barbara Heller

I agree with most of Professor White's paper—indeed I think it was excellent—but I would not want to agree with all of it and hurt his credibility. Moreover, I agree with Mr. Jackson that the short-and-medium-term OCS oil, rather than coal and oil shale, is the environmentally superior way of meeting energy needs. But I think that some of the other sources have been given too short shrift. When we speak of using coal resources, the general assumption is that it will be strip-mined coal, and therefore much more damaging than OCS drilling. But that is not necessarily a fair assumption, particularly if the President does not veto the strip-mining bill.

We have heard deep-water ports compared as an alternative several times. But I do not think we have a true either/or question at this point. I think we will have both OCS development and deep-water ports. The question is how we are going to bring in oil and develop oil in some rational manner. The environmental groups that I have worked with do not oppose offshore oil development, but we feel very strongly that offshore oil does not have to be developed at an accelerated rate and we feel very strongly that it should be administered in a new way.

One of the ways we think would represent an improvement in the system is federal exploration. Mr. Jackson talked about the lack of everything that goes into separating exploration from development. I think we should note that separation has been tried in other places, that the Dutch government would not grant a license for production until it was sure a commercial find would be produced. I do not think that is something done in ignorance over there in the North Sea. In any case let me explain why we favor federal exploration, because I think it is a critical point in the argument over the rate of development.

If information is gathered before production actually begins, the Department of the Interior can make rational leasing decisions based both on the energy resource potential and on the value of other resources in the area, including fishing resources, and on the environmental risks involved. The states would have time to develop coastal zone management plans and to plan for the environmental impact before production leasing occurs. How can we expect the state to plan for the effects that occur with offshore development if the state does not know the extent of the offshore resources? Moreover, the information would be available to the public, so that while the states and communities planned, the public could comment in an informed manner on the potential effects of development as the Environmental Policy Act intended. The independent oil producers would have more information on which to base their leasing decisions, and less risk. The independents would increase leasing competition, which would produce increased revenues for the federal treasury.

A federal exploration system—meaning a contractual system, not one in which the Department of the Interior would go out and do the exploring itself—probably would result in quicker development than the current policies, which, from all indications, are going to be hung up in the courts for years. It has become clear over the last several months that the states will no longer tolerate being brought in after the decisions have been made in Washington.

The Coastal States Organization, the National Governors Conference, the Conference of State Legislatures, and the East Coast governors have all come out with strong statements favoring a more rational Department of the Interior program, including some separation of exploration and production and calling for a pause to develop the studies called for by the Coastal Zone Management Act. I do not think that we are going to be able to play off the coastal states against each other, as had been suggested earlier. I think we need a new program. I also do not think—to go back to the revenue-sharing question—that it is going to be quite so easy as some have suggested to "buy off" the states. Revenue sharing is not going to be the answer. Certainly some states may be willing to be "bought off," but I think for the most part those who are running the coastal states—for example, California and Massachusetts, and perhaps Governor Byrne can speak about New Jersey—now may care about the money, because none of the states are in very good financial shape, but I think they also care about their coastlines and what is going to happen when the inevitable effects of offshore development occur.

I would like to finish with a question about refineries as they relate to OCS development on the East Coast. Perhaps Professor White can answer this or perhaps Mr. Jackson can. In any case, we have had, over the last few years, varied estimates of how many refineries are going to be needed on the East Coast. A year and a half ago, we were told we would need dozens of refineries to produce refined oil on the East Coast. The latest statement from the Department of the Interior and from the companies is that we will not need any new refineries to cope with OCS development, since OCS development is going to be replacing imported oil. I do not believe that statement. I would like to know whether the companies really believe we will not need any more refineries—whether the refineries that now exist on the East Coast will be able to cope with that OCS crude. Are most of the refineries on the East Coast only able to handle sour crude or sweet crude, and what is expected of the offshore oil here? I think it is an important question, because refineries are certainly one of the key parts of coastal development.

Let me conclude by saying I think OCS accelerated development is not only undesirable but even unobtainable, because of the constraints Professor White mentioned—the shortages of equipment, labor and capital—and because of the opposition of the states, and the fact that studies will not have been done under current leasing procedures before production occurs. I would hope that the Department of the Interior will begin to work with those at the state and local level and with private groups to try to come up with some programs that will include the public in the planning process.

Richard Perrine

In his paper, Professor White has put forth what I consider quite reasonable proposals as an answer to the crucial question he was asked. Of the many points in his paper that merit discussion, I would like to focus attention on one, and to note salient features of some others.

Perhaps the most effective way to introduce what I consider an essential part of the primary question is to pose it in this fashion: What is the appropriate rate of education and professional preparation of petroleum engineers and other key energy industry personnel?

This topic was addressed at the October 1974 meeting of the Education and Accreditation Committee of the Society of Petroleum Engineers. The discussion during that open meeting showed quite clearly that the need for skilled professionals is irrevocably tied to the rate of offshore development. Perhaps a little history will show how and why.

Petroleum exploration, drilling, and production operations are not labor-intensive activities. A relatively small number of skilled individuals do the job. At one time recruiters for the industry proudly proclaimed that they had an interest only in the top 15 percent or so of any graduating class. I may say they often got something less. When times were economically difficult, it seemed simple and natural for the industry not to hire new employees, and even to release some long-time employees, so that they could seek out a more useful role elsewhere in our society. This was done with an apparent total disregard for long-term technical staffing needs.

A direct consequence of this approach was that in the late 1950s, when jobs in petroleum were scarce, there was a drastic decline in petroleum engineering enrollments, reaching a low level that held steady for a long time. A natural concomitant of this was a decline in petroleum engineering faculty both in numbers and in overall quality measured by the established academic criteria for professionally oriented staff. Another direct consequence was the closure or reorganization of many petroleum educational activities. Of course, after several years, petroleum industry economics recovered and the industry again knocked on academic doors, seeking qualified new technical staff. Unfortunately, there were few to be had.

Today the picture is much improved so far as petroleum students are concerned; about 2,000 U.S. and 1,000 foreign undergraduates are enrolled in petroleum engineering studies. But note Dr. White's estimate of need: 10,000 added petroleum engineers. Considering overseas requirements as well, in the near term we certainly are seeking something more than twenty years' worth of new engineers at the relatively high present rate of production.

One further question should be raised. Has faculty growth kept pàce with the resurgence of student enrollment? The answer is a resounding no. Petroleum departments have historically been small, they have often been academically weak and have been seriously harmed by the former ups and down in demand for their services. What happens to a petroleum department with three faculty members and hundreds of students if one faculty member is even temporarily incapacitated? What kind of balanced and thorough education can be provided if a staff of even five must simultaneously be expert in reservoir engineering, offshore technology, production operations and well stimulation, fluid mechanics, formation evaluation, drilling and rock mechanics, gas technology, operations research, and computer simulation? The answer is, of course, that students are exposed to a smattering of everything, with a bit more than a smattering where it can be offered, and come out less than well prepared.

Now, faculty members could be added, except that most good people would not accept the requisite pay and working conditions. No one has offered to foot the increased bill necessary to attract more staff. One private southern California institution estimates that the faculty positions that should be added represent a current commitment of $750,000. That is a totally unreachable sum in today's academic environment especially when we are looking forward to a 25 percent decline in overall enrollments within a few years. Certainly no oil company, nor any federal, state or other source, has offered annual payment of this sum to solve the question of staff and ensure qualified future manpower.

Not everything in the professional situation of petroleum specialists is this bleak. The Society of Petroleum Engineers has long had one of the best planned, most widely utilized, and probably most effective continuing education programs of any professional group. In addition, many of the larger oil companies operate their own schools. But on the basis of my own years of personal involvement in exactly these kinds of activities, as well as in basic engineering education, I must argue that though they supplement, they cannot replace an original high-quality education. There is no substitute for continuing contact with people with the right kind of background and for quality throughout those formative undergraduate years.

Thus, it would appear reasonable to conclude that a substantial period of time may have elapsed before large numbers of qualified professionals are prepared to manage enlarged and technically difficult OCS operations in a skillful way. If a serious effort were made with proper financial support, perhaps five years would see the schools in much better shape; another five years would provide the time required for the educational process to function and to provide well-prepared graduates; and a final five years of seasoning through job experience would provide individuals prepared to assume responsibility for large-scale operations within critical OCS areas.

To jump into offshore operations without this reservoir of qualified individuals would be, in my judgment, the single action most likely to lead to another Santa Barbara Channel platform. And the perceived result of a major spill during the early days of renewed offshore oil operations in California, regardless of the real long-term impact, might well spell doom for further offshore operations. This should not be allowed to happen. This means a gradual buildup to enlarged activities by (let us say) 1990, not an instantaneous jump to the OCS tomorrow. There is no need, in these circumstances, for accelerated offshore leasing.

I believe the other constraints mentioned by Professor White, the shortages of capital, materials, equipment, and management capability, and the need for development of valid and reasonably complete scientific background information

110

for OCS leases, lead to a similar conclusion. But if I advance arguments for the deliberate rather than accelerated buildup toward new domestic energy sources, it is only proper for someone to ask what alternatives might be proposed within this same time frame which would permit our society to function.

Over the past year at UCLA, we have studied problems of population and energy in Los Angeles through the work of a multidisciplinary team. Transportation was a key sector within which we searched for alternative futures. Our results in this sector assume no greater intensity of effort than that proposed to develop OCS oil, and certainly no higher costs or need for technology. Yet they indicate that by 1990 we could probably achieve a 40 percent reduction in energy requirements for transportation in Los Angeles from conventional extrapolations. This would mean savings of perhaps 150,000 barrels of oil per day for this metropolitan area. We assumed no loss of mobility, retaining a projected value of about 22.6 person-miles per day. We also assumed that all emissions control requirements for every vehicle would be met. We believe the results we developed are achievable and that they could gain societal acceptance. Along with other alternatives, this would provide a different future we could choose in place of an accelerated search for more energy followed by its continued wasteful use.

In conclusion, it is obvious that no decision can be reached on the proper pace of offshore oil development until we have a workable and well-thought-out national energy policy. We have a very wide range of choices before us. Searching for an optimal pace requires that we first establish a hierarchy of feasible alternatives and note their constraints, and then carefully search by iterative multi-level techniques for a globally optimal future path.

One thing I would like to note here is that if we look into ecology, we immediately find ecologists saying there is stability in diversity. If we are to have a stable future in terms of energy supply, we are not going to depend primarily on one source; we are going to look for as many feasible alternatives as possible to mix together. In other words, we are not going to put all our energy eggs in one basket.

The process of finding such an optimal future cannot be quick if it is going to be thorough. Pilot operations, such as offshore exploration, must be used carefully to provide an empirical data base. The alternative is to continue to blunder until our next miscalculation sends another major shock wave through our entire system. Given this evaluation, I find myself in total agreement with the final paragraph in Dr. White's paper.

Irvin L. White

I appreciate Professor Perrine's illumination of the personnel constraints. I really have no other comment on his remarks. As for Ms. Heller's question, I do not know the answer about refineries. I agree that deep mining is a possibility, and I think it is problematic as to whether the states can, in fact, be "bought off."

My major comment on the comments leads me back to the central theme with which I began my remarks—that is, what we are talking about here and what is being debated as a matter of national policy must be considered within the total context in which we make these kinds of decisions. My response to Mr. Jackson must be that "business as usual" is not a true alternative. The thrust of my remarks was intended to indicate that the oil industry, the regulatory agencies, the executive branch, and, for that matter, the Congress, do not have as a true alternative the ignoring of the new participants who are demanding entry into decision making in this area.

As a consequence, it is not so much a question of "buying off" the states or a question of dealing with the kind of physical and personnel constraints we talked about, as it is a question of how we will manage to work out a political accommodation that satisfies the needs of the major participants in the policy system. That is my point about the current administration and its insistence on the accelerated leasing program and, apparently, its unwillingness to seek accommodations that would provide for a greater state role in planning future OCS development. In the long run progress without accommodations will be impossible. What the states will do is slow the rate of OCS development. What we ought to be engaged in is an attempt to work out the accommodations that will satisfy legitimate interests in the process of determining a pace for OCS development.

While, as Mr. Solomon pointed out, scientific and legal analyses are certainly important ingredients, we need to illuminate the consequences, in the long term, of making one political decision as compared to making another. In our political system what we do is make decisions that satisfy a variety of interests: when we choose between alternatives, we do not choose the one that offers the greatest net expectation in social benefits, but the one that is politically feasible. And at the present time political feasibility must be determined by the various parties and interests, some of which have not been involved in OCS development in the past, but are now demanding representation in making policy.

DISCUSSION

MR. JACKSON: On Ms. Heller's question on refineries, let me try to make clear under what circumstances refineries are normally built, where they are built, and why they are built. First, we do not consider refineries an integral part of offshore exploration and production. Refineries are a product of consumer demands. If the consumer wants more jet fuel, more gasoline, more heating oil, he will demand this and the refineries will have to be enlarged to meet his demand. The fact that we have offshore oil does not create a need for refineries per se. We believe firmly that any oil found on the East Coast would tend to back out imports from foreign sources on a barrel-for-barrel basis.

Now, let me hasten to say that this does not mean we do not need additional refineries on the East Coast or that we will not need new refineries in the United States in the future. We will because our demand is going to continue to grow. We will need new refinery capacity, both from building new refineries and through the expansion of existing capacity. Today most companies are expanding existing capacity, because it is much simpler to do this than to fight all the red tape and the environmental groups that want to thwart our efforts to build new refineries. My company and many others are therefore expanding internally.

Let me make two or three other points if I may. The comments were made that mobile rigs would be a problem, and it was said that in the "MAFLA" area there should be twenty-six and now there are only a few. The reason that there are only a few there is that we have, up to this point, drilled seven dry holes and are drilling an eighth. If there were some production, there would be more rigs. We were assured just last week by several of the major drilling contractors that they have mobile rigs available. We were also assured by one of the major platform fabricators that space is available to build platforms. There are no constraints in that sense.

Another factor that has come into play is the necessary time to plan: I would like to take a moment to quantify some of the remarks that have been made. Everyone speaks about the size of the effects of offshore development. I would like to quantify them for you, according to our judgment. These are not to be taken as absolutely final, but they are in the ball park. I would like to give you the numbers we think would be involved in a production rate of 500,000 barrels of oil and 750 million cubic feet of gas a day in the East Coast and the mid-Atlantic.

Now, the dollars I am going to give are 1974 Louisiana dollars. This takes into consideration the use of thirty rigs, ten mobiles and twenty development rigs. It involves either two large service facilities with some sixty-five companies in each one of them or else having these facilities scattered throughout the fifty platform operations. It means four production bases, four offices, three gas processing plants, three pipeline terminals, and one platform construction facility. All this activity would involve about 4,600 people, of which we estimate 65 percent would be employed locally and trained by the company. This would mean a payroll of about $8.5 million a month. The operation would use 900 acres, and this would be scattered over the whole mid-Atlantic from New York to Virginia. Now, those are the numbers we are talking about, and to me they are not massive numbers. In fact, this represents a pretty small impact. After all the mid-Atlantic area has about 37 million people or about 18 percent of the United States population, and the net population gain in that area every day is about 7,000 people. We are talking about adding a net of 35 percent of the 4,600—that is, 1,600 people—over a period of five to seven years. I do not think this requires a tremendous amount of planning. I think it requires going out and picking the spot where a man can build a little office facility or a place where he can have two boats or a heliport.

I think such development needs to be carried out. I think the states can already plan for such development. I think that between the time that an oil field is discovered—and I am talking about one oil field, not a whole string of them—and the time the companies can design and construct a platform, put that platform in, drill the development wells, and install a pipeline and delivery system, there is ample time for this planning process to take place.

MS. HELLER: Mr. Jackson's 900-acre figure puzzles me. If that is for all those facilities, why did Brown and Root just buy 2,000 acres for a platform fabrication facility?

MR. JACKSON: In my calculation, I allowed them 400, which is more than they wanted. To get what they wanted, they had to buy the 2,000, including the golf course, which they did not really want.

PROFESSOR DEVANNEY: This is a rare opportunity for me to agree with J.R. The onshore effects have been grossly overstated, mainly as a result of Resource Planning Associates' work done for the Council on Environmental Quality. Our own numbers are an order of magnitude less than the figures that showed up in the CEQ report. We do not know how they got those numbers.

MS. HELLER: Are Professor Devanney's employment figures anything like Mr. Jackson's figures?

PROFESSOR DEVANNEY: They are much closer to his than they are to CEQ's.

114

MS. HELLER: The CEQ figures were huge.

MR. JACKSON: Let me add one other comment here. This goes back to the separation of exploration from production. In the American Association of Petroleum Geologists, we keep statistics on field sizes, number of new fields, and wildcats drilled. We do not even give a value to a field's reserves until the field has been explored and developed for six years. Our data from the period 1961 to 1965 indicate that it takes 1,654 wells to find a 50-million-barrel field or the gas equivalent, which is 300 billion cubic feet. That is the kind of an effort we are talking about. Let me add that this is nationwide. It will not be that bad offshore, but it will certainly be something tremendously larger than going out and drilling a dozen wells or two dozen wells or even 200 wells and finding all that.

DR. GASKINS: I would like to clarify a few things for the record. First, the administration is no longer committed to selling 10 million acres a year. In 1974, the President announced in conjunction with the secretary of the interior that, because of some of the problems that have been raised here, the administration was backing away from this figure and that our tentative schedule would be six sales a year of indeterminate size. To place that in perspective, I may say that this year we have sold roughly 600,000 acres. We will offer for sale over the rest of the year 6.4 million acres. If we sold it all, which is extremely unlikely, we would still be talking about less than 7 million acres. It is clear there is some lack of communication between what the administration is saying and the program is doing, on the one hand, and some of the belated reports that are now coming out, on the other hand.

There is a second point I would like to emphasize. There has been considerable talk about government exploration programs. I think anyone who is serious about this question should make sure he defines for himself what he is talking about, because there is a host of programs we could embark upon, from drilling one or two stratigraphic holes to exclusive control of the exploration process by the federal government. We have done some work on this in the Department of the Interior and are continuing our work, and we would like to enter into a dialogue on the advantages and disadvantages of various programs. But I would like to warn everyone about the alternative of giving the federal government exclusive control of all exploration activities on the OCS. I notice Professor Perrine's comment that in ecology diversity is a good thing. If we look at exploration around the world, diversity is a good thing. The conventional wisdom on where gas and oil will be found is wrong more often than it is right. My reading of history is that if we are going to find oil in an efficient way, we should encourage everyone who has any idea on how to find oil and gas to go out and look. I think reserving exclusive exploration rights to the federal government would be a serious mistake.

115

PROFESSOR DEVANNEY: Do you imply that the Department of the Interior is moving towards something less than exclusive exploration rights for private industry?

DR. GASKINS: We are always considering alternatives.

MR. SOLOMON: I would like to ask a question of Mr. Jackson. He had some harsh words for the separation of exploration from production, but perhaps in simple terms we are talking about two different models. One is a model which we could label federal exploration, which, in fact, contains a range of half a dozen different strategies, as Dr. Gaskins mentioned. The second is an entirely different approach which, for a short title, we might call a two-title system. The latter is advanced by CEQ, and under it, industry would be given a permit to explore, and would conduct its exploration activities on what I would hope would be a normal basis. Then separate consideration would be given to issuance of a production permit at a later stage. I know that technically this is something that already exists under present regulations, but perhaps the separation is not quite so clear and so formal as could be under this system.

In objecting to the separation of exploration from production, is Mr. Jackson objecting to the separation per se, or is he reacting to the idea of federal management of exploration activity? Specifically, in his view, could industry live with a version of the separation of exploration from production on the basis of a two-title system, rather than a federal manager system?

MR. JACKSON: No. It would take the incentive out of doing business: we could go out and buy war bonds and do just as well. We are a risk-oriented business: we take risks for a living. I would hate to be in the position of the government manager who had to explain the fact that he had drilled 100 straight dry holes—or even five straight dry holes—to a senator who had just told his constituency he was going to solve this problem.

The other point I would emphasize is that this separation would cause a great delay in production activities. I do not think we can make it any more clear than we have that the problem here is one of time: we need to get on with this job as fast as we can. It will take at least three to five years to get into substantial production, and that is probably a conservative number. If we include a two- or three-year program of exploring, we will still not get the answers we need in that period of time, and we will delay production. A significant offshore field would be one in the range of 50 million barrels off the East Coast or off the Gulf of Alaska. To find a field of this kind, we will have to spend a lot of time, a lot of money, and drill a lot of wells. I think, as Dr. Gaskins indicated, this can best be done by a large number of people using a wide variety of talent and experience and expertise. Furthermore, if we did find a field, there would be nearly irresistible pressure for

116

the federal government to develop it. This would mean a whole new ball game, and it would result in nationalization. If we are going to nationalize the oil industry, why not nationalize steel and autos and all the rest? We think federal exploration would be the beginning step to the end of a free enterprise system in this country.

PROFESSOR MENARD: It seems to me Mr. Jackson is facing the responsibility of answering questions when he might have expected to be a discussant. While I disagree in principle with many of the things he has been saying, I want to make a comment on his figures on the success ratio on drilling for oil. It takes a number of holes to get a significant field; but it takes only about seven holes to get a show of oil.

MR. JACKSON: Five.

PROFESSOR MENARD: It may be five this year. In any case the figure I remember is that the chance of finding a commercial oil or gas field is about one in thirty, which is a long way from 1,654.

MR. JACKSON: Over the period of time we are talking about, it took sixty-one holes to find a field of 1 million barrels or the gas equivalent of 30 billion cubic feet. All the statistics are here, but let me hasten to say, as I did before, that these apply to all the wells drilled in the United States. Professor Menard is right in what he is saying, but these numbers are so far as I know absolutely accurate; they come from the American Association of Petroleum Geologists, and we have to depend on them.

PROFESSOR MENARD: I think the important point—and the one thing on which we are in complete agreement—is that the success rate declines every year. We get less and less oil, a smaller number of oil fields, in drilling the same amount every year.

MR. JACKSON: That is right. It takes more wells each year.

ROBERT CAHN, The Conservation Foundation: Just a couple points that have been building up for a long time. One point concerns Dr. Mead's remarks. I think he said we must assume that the cost of the delay may be traced to the environmentalists, and that this is the only cost involved. I think he could equally say that if in 1969 the permit had been given to build the Alaskan pipeline, we might have found greater costs in the fact that we were not prepared to build the pipeline at that time. The Department of the Interior has since admitted we were not ready and there might have been some disasters along the way, economic as well as to the wildlife and the terrain. I think there was another very basic thing we did not look at. We did not look at the responsibility involved in using the oil up now and not having it for future generations. Without looking at some of these ethical questions, we just assumed that we need it all because it would be terrible to import.

PROFESSOR MEAD: I agree entirely with your comments on the trans-Alaskan pipeline. I think it is well understood that the Alyeska Company had not done its homework by the time it submitted that proposal, and it had to change a lot of things. But that was not quite the point I was addressing. The point I was addressing is regulations that involve expensive compliance—a billion dollars or so—must be cost justified, and they were not.

As to Mr. Cahn's point, using oil now as against using it in the future, I agree this is a question that has never been addressed. The federal government is the owner of our resources and our grandchildren's resources. The federal government puts them out for lease and industry buys as it wishes to buy. So far as I know, and Dr. Gaskins may correct me, there has never been a study made by the Department of the Interior on the question: what is the optimum rate of leasing of our resources over time?

I think it is true that last year the Department of the Interior leased about 5.5 million acres. A year or two before that, I think about 500,000 acres were leased. When President Nixon came out with his figure of 10 million, he was responding to pressures. The federal government is the outfit that is in charge of our resources, and I do not believe the government is allocating these resources in any rational manner.

MR. REILLY: I would like to add something on that point, if I might. When this OCS program was begun with such urgency, it was believed that there was a great shortage of oil in the world. In the last several months, we have been hearing that there may be a glut. The *Economist* predicted this glut a year ago, and now there appears to be some evidence that what the *Economist* said may be true. As Dr. Gaskins responds to that question, perhaps he could respond to this one, too. What effect will the possibility of a glut have on the decision of the Department of the Interior whether to accelerate offshore leasing? I know it has been suggested that the department should, at least in the North Sea, get the oil and gas while the price is still high. Does a glut suggest the same kind of thing, in your opinion, in this country?

DR. GASKINS: Mr. Reilly has asked some questions whose answers are quite complicated. I will first try to touch on some of the facts of the matter and then try to make some argument. The facts are that the leasing rate has jumped around, but that the jumps have not been quite as dramatic as Dr. Mead suggested. Two years ago the figure was a million acres. Last year we leased 2 million acres. I gave you the figures for this year earlier. Now, the public statements on what we would like to lease have been tripling and tripling, but we never reach those figures. Those are basically target figures for planning purposes.

There have been some studies done on what the appropriate rate of leasing is, but most of those here—except perhaps Dr. Mead (if I got him in a corner)—would not find the studies very palatable, because what we have in mind is that there are certain backstop technologies that in the intermediate run (say within fifty years) will provide other sources of energy to us. We have centuries of coal left. We have lots of shale. We have a tremendous investment in research and development in nuclear power. We look down the road around fifty years, and perhaps sooner than that, and there are other technologies that will come in at a price that is difficult to estimate, though we know they will be more costly than oil.

Our studies indicate that these backstops are particularly likely to come in if we diversify our investment portfolio in R & D, and that the proper government policy is to lease as rapidly as possible, consistent with protecting the environment and fair market value of the resource. The reason is that the federal government's slow leasing rate in the past has been responsible for our not having taken advantage of the resources we have.

It is true that economists have been talking about a coming oil glut for a long time, but the cartel has maintained the $11.00 price. Unfortunately, a lot of the additions in the reserves around the world are occurring in reserves held by members of OPEC. Saudi Arabia remains a dominant force in the oil market. It would be pleasant if the price of oil went back down to $2.00. We would have serious questions whether we would wish to bail out anyone who had taken a flyer on the expectation of $7.00 oil, but the probability that the price will fall is conditional on what we do. If the United States does not do anything about its energy situation, if it continues to import a growing percentage of its oil, it will make it easier and easier for the cartel to maintain the price.

The economic modeling in the case of this particular cartel is naive: I do not think this is a cartel of the sort we have seen before. If we look at studies of cartels, we find that they normally last a year or two years. They are generally unsuccessful and break up with a lot of bickering. But this is both a politically inspired cartel and a very asymmetrical cartel—Saudi Arabia has a tremendous share of that oil. For our foreign policy and for our national security, it is dangerous for us to assume naively that next year the price of oil will go down to $2.00 a barrel and that we do not have to develop any alternatives.

CAPTAIN COUSTEAU: I think I agree with Dr. Gaskins. Since the beginning of this conference, everyone has assumed, without giving any explanation, that we must go very fast in exploration for oil. It was like an axiom that no one has ever substantiated with any serious figures.

I am sure I would be called emotional if I were to talk about the interests of our children and our grandchildren; so I will not. But as a member of the Western community of nations I am interested in the strategic problem involved in oil. It seems to me that Project Independence—about which I immediately sent a cable to President Nixon, in the name of my society—was a mistake, because it held that the energy independence of this country was more important today than tomorrow. I think that was a big mistake, because today we are in a period of relative peace. Tensions are not very high, and we can afford to buy some external oil. Perhaps in twenty years, the situation will be different, and at that time, we will have nothing of our own to fulfill our needs.

I think that the strategic problem has not really been discussed, that it is very complicated, and that it does not, I am sorry to say, belong entirely to the federal government. It belongs to the people, and the federal government is made up of people who are in office four or five years, perhaps eight years, while these problems will go on for twenty or twenty-five years; the housewives may be more interested in the future of their children than the high-ranking public servants are interested in the future of any country.

Now, there is something that is systematically understated in our Western press, because we are used to hearing the statements of our leaders contradicted the following week. Hitler, for example, when he wrote *Mein Kampf*, announced clearly what was going on, but no one believed him until he carried through. He attacked the Western world and put us in World War II. We have the same thing with the Shah of Iran, who has said systematically, Hurry up, Western world, develop other sources of energy, because in ten years we will turn off the faucet. No one takes this seriously, unfortunately, but I think it is very serious. I think the members of OPEC are now using the money from oil exports to develop their own economy, to sell us finished products and no more oil. They are preparing to do so and we are helping them to do so. If the United States is not going to buy the oil, Germany will, because the Western world is divided. In this general context, I think the proper strategy of the Western world should be to think not of today but tomorrow.

Alternative sources of energy have been studied. I have here a vast collection of documents by my group on these things. Alternative sources of energy exist in the form of coal, tar sands, shale oil, and so on. We know that. But all of these sources are nonrenewable and they have an environmental impact much greater than offshore oil would have.

Before I go to the possibilities of solar energy, and to my job which is largely studying the sun concentrated in the sea, I would like to state that I am not basically opposed from the environmental standpoint to offshore drilling. I am a constructive environmentalist. I am, if you wish, a witness. I have been at sea very often, diving very often, and I know exactly what happens in the sea today with oil pollution. It is not very bad; it is disagreeable, but it is not very bad. The beaches all around the world are polluted, it is true, and as someone said today, it is disagreeable to walk and have dirty feet, but that is about all the effect.

120

It is often said by the oil companies that the derricks and the platforms are shelters for fish and encourage the concentration of fish. It is true. These structures, like any kind of sunken ship, like wood, attract fish. There is no difference, basically, in the world of the fish between an oil derrick and a sunken ship, and I do not think the presence of some oil there would impair the congregation of fish. The same thing holds for what Mr. Savit said this morning; we did not need the Russians to know that the Sargasso Sea remains the clearest sea in the world.

Nevertheless, there is one thing that must not be neglected and that is the damage done by oil to the surface of the ocean. Today it is almost impossible to study neuston, which are the animals living in the very upper layer of the ocean. There is nowhere in the ocean to throw a neuston net without bringing in a layer of contaminated surface. Certainly there are some unknown consequences along the line. I agree entirely with Dr. Menard that we need many years to really understand what we are doing to the environment. The damage that an oil spill can do is a result of its concentration. It comes not from the quantity of oil released, but from the size of the surface of the oil slick. Disasters these are, but they are temporary and they are local. By contrast, a nuclear plant explosion would be a disaster affecting a large area. We have to make a distinction between the two and we prefer offshore oil to nuclear industry with no hesitation.

This being said, what are the alternatives?

The clean alternative is the sun's energy. Now, Btus and watts are units that confuse the mind because they are jumbled with tremendous figures. As a practical unit I prefer the unit of a large nuclear plant: 1,000 megawatts. The average large nuclear plant produces 1,000 megawatts. Today the amount of energy we are producing worldwide is only one-ten-thousandth of what the sun's energy gives to the planet. Some of this energy is reflected, some is absorbed, mainly (70 percent) into the sea. The potential energy absorbed by the earth is on the order of 70 million nuclear plants. This energy is concentrated by ocean currents in some areas where it is relatively easy to exploit. The United States is blessed by the fact that, first, it has large deserts with lots of insulation, and, second, in the Straits of Florida it has the best of all areas of concentrated marine thermal energy. The United States has the very best potential for the development of solar energy in the entire world. If one-ten-thousandth of the energy absorbed by the sea were converted into electricity—and we know how to do that—it would be the equivalent of 50,000 nuclear plants, which means four times all the energy the world burns today. That could be taken from the Florida Straits, which means that the United States could be exporting energy in the form of liquid hydrogen in vast quantities. I have all the figures here about solar energy that could be exploited, but I will not bore my listeners with it.

I am the chairman of Eurocean, which is the union of all the major European industries interested in the development of the sea. We have estimated that to develop a solar energy system that would provide about half the needs of the

121

United States in fifteen years would take $1 trillion. Now, $1 trillion seems to be a fantastic amount of money. In fact, it is not much when we consider that the cost of the long-range nuclear program is $850 billion and that $3 trillion has been spent on other energy around the world. One trillion dollars in fifteen years is a vast sum of money but perfectly within the scale of U.S. possibilities. This would give the United States, in fifteen years, total energy independence, and the United States would become an exporter of energy.

I have some additional figures to make the picture a lot more palatable, but I do not have time to expand on them. Solar energy is not a fantasy: it is based on hard facts. The fact is that one of these plants, one very crude plant, actually worked in Cuba in 1929. We know how to use solar energy and since 1929, of course, technology has provided improvements to this system. By combining the new solar cells, which have a very high efficiency, with the thermal differences in the sea, the United States could be completely independent in energy. If such investments were made, I think we environmentalists would support a temporary bridging of the energy gap by exploiting offshore oil. But I think we would not like to commit ourselves to support if the federal government were not committed to the development of solar energy on a large scale.

DR. RADLINSKI: The estimates of the U.S. Geological Survey seem to be a concern to a lot of people. The Geological Survey does not make official estimates of resources; there is no such animal as an official U.S. Geological Survey estimate. Rather USGS scientists make their own independent estimates of resources. We should not overlook the fact that the National Research Council recently considered nine estimates of resources. Of those nine, five came from Geological Survey employees, including the high and the low estimates; but, for some reason the readers want to associate the high figure with the Geological Survey, and they forget that the low also came from us. Now, it does not really matter which figure we consider as far as policy is concerned, because either figure tells us that there is a lot of oil and gas out there to be explored and to be developed, and simple mathematics will show that if we have a billion years' supply of any commodity at current use and we use it at an increasing annual rate of 3 percent, that billion years' supply will be depleted in 584 years. Take the high estimates of 300 to 500 billion barrels of oil. Assume that consumption will continue to increase 3 percent annually. That increase means that we will have depleted the oil in from forty-eight to eighty years. If we increase at the rate that we have increased it on the average for the past twenty years, it will be depleted in from twenty-eight to thirty-seven years. That, in itself, speaks to the question whether we should decide what to do about the petroleum out there. And it should point out that it does not matter whether we consider the high figure or the low figure: public petroleum policy has to be made now.

122

MR. MATTHEWS: It has been a stimulating day. I was probably one of the most provocative persons here today, and I admit I did it deliberately. I was more positive for Ms. Heller's benefit than I would have been in her absence. I have one very brief observation here. In my discussion with Professor Menard this morning, I made the point—I hope rather strongly—that the U.S. Geological Survey, the federal government, as the keeper of the public interest, has the right to get the oil field exploration data just the same as the oil companies or anyone else does. The answer came back that the director of the U.S. Geological Survey says the public will not give the USGS the money to do it. My point is that if Congress, in its infinite wisdom, being a political organization, will not provide a few million dollars to buy these data, what in the hell makes us think Congress will spend hundreds of millions of dollars to drill dry wells in the OCS?

MR. REILLY: I guess I have not heard the word infinite used in Washington, at least not about wisdom.

PROFESSOR MEAD: I have a number of points, some of them from way back in the discussion. This business of the cartel price keeps coming up. What will happen to the price of oil? I look around the world, and I see that on the supply side and on the demand side things are happening just as the economic textbooks say they should happen. The price of oil has quadrupled in three years and demand has fallen off. I suspect that the long-run elasticity of demand is such that there will be no growth in demand if the price stays up, and demand could very well fall off further. Over on the supply side, the theory says that supply reacts to price, and—lo and behold!—there is considerable evidence that supply does react. Some of the evidence may be fortuitous, but look at what is happening.

In the North Sea, every time the developers restake reserves, they double them again. Now the companies are talking about 5 million barrels a day by 1980. Let us take that as a fact. Then we find talk coming out of reasonable and responsible circles, about Chinese reserves being found equal to those of Saudi Arabia, around 140 billion barrels. I do not know whether we want to believe that or not. I myself am skeptical. But then we go to Mexico, and we find a big new field down there. We do not know how big, but big. Iraq talks about floating on a sea of oil under Baghdad. Off Brazil we are finding oil. I have a strong feeling that there is no way the cartel can survive beyond 1980. Darius Gaskins points out that this is a different breed of cartel. There is an OAPEC contingent in which there is considerable unity, but that is not enough to produce cartel effects. OPEC itself is more diverse than any of those oligopolies we have studied in the past; and given supply and demand factors, I will be willing to bet anyone a stake that by 1979 it is a defunct cartel.

CAPTAIN COUSTEAU: I will take the bet, because I think the people who are in command of the cartel are not going to be reasonable.

PROFESSOR MEAD: I grant that some of them are not.

CAPTAIN COUSTEAU: Most of them are basically very politically oriented. They have a flag and an ideal, and they are going to act in a way we call irrational and they call rational. I am quite sure they will not close the cartel.

DR. RADLINSKI: May I just say one thing. As of December 1974 an order from the secretary of the interior has required all permittees to provide any information that they collect to the Geological Survey upon request within thirty days.

MR. KNECHT: Does that include analysis of the data?

PROFESSOR MENARD: Do you have a computer access system for obtaining data from your voluminous collection?

DR. RADLINSKI: That has to be developed, and development is a matter of money.

PART FIVE

Offshore Oil: Costs and Benefits

The televised panel discussion concluding the conference began with the question of the urgency of offshore development. One view was that these resources should be husbanded for more perilous international times, while another suggested that a second oil embargo could come at any time. Criticism of the government's accelerated development program met the response that to delay the program until each difficulty was resolved would risk another energy shortage. Is the choice between off-shore drilling and importing oil in supertankers? It was explained that while offshore oil will displace some imports, foreign oil will still be needed. Greatly improved safety was noted in offshore operations since the Santa Barbara spill and it was agreed that spills from supertankers have done far more damage than those from drilling. The Department of the Interior was described as opposed to the government's taking over exploration for offshore oil but as seeking a way to separate industry exploration and production into two operations. Governor Byrne suggested that the states might want to get into the oil business.

ROUND TABLE DISCUSSION

MAYOR BRADLEY, moderator of the Round Table: I am delighted to welcome to Los Angeles AEI's National Energy Project and this important discussion of the energy problem. In my view, it is appropriate that we should come to Los Angeles to talk about "Offshore Oil, Costs and Benefits."

We have a distinguished panel to discuss this matter: First, Mr. H. J. Haynes, chairman of the board and chief executive officer of the Standard Oil Company of California; second, Captain Jacques-Yves Cousteau, internationally known explorer, philosopher, and poet, and a distinguished television performer and producer who opened up for millions the world under the sea. Also on our panel are the governor of New Jersey, the Honorable Brendan Byrne, and Assistant Secretary of the Interior Royston Hughes.

Governor Byrne, would you begin the discussion this morning?

GOVERNOR BYRNE: The subjects under discussion here are the costs and benefits associated with offshore oil and gas development. Usually the governors of the coastal states do not see eye to eye on any subject, but on this subject, I think, there is close to unanimous agreement within our group that we ought to proceed with development only after gaining full knowledge as to its implications. We want to know what will be going on if the development of offshore oil occurs.

Let me state how I and the other coastal governors would go about the development of a resource under the ocean near our coastlines, especially the coastlines of states sensitive to development. If we did not know what our federal government was doing, we would try to get as much information as possible from it. We would ask the oil companies to pool their resources to gather what information they could and provide it to us. Then, using all that information, with whatever we could get from our federal government, we would proceed very cautiously, but in an orderly step-by-step manner, using a rational plan to develop those offshore oil and gas resources. We would want to know what the effects would be on the ocean, what the effects would be onshore, and what would be the best way of minimizing or eliminating those effects.

In contrast, the worst possible thing to do would be to divide the offshore region into a series of huge tracts and put those tracts out for bidding, and then to say that the highest bidder would get a shot at both exploring and developing

127

those tracts without any additional scrutiny. In other words, once the bid was out, good luck. I think the federal government is using a procedure a lot closer to this than to the rational plan, and many of us—many of the governors of the coastal states—have raised our voices against that.

I think we have made some progress. I think Mr. Hughes and Mr. Morton are beginning to see the dangers in putting huge areas out for bidding under the current scheme. I would emphasize that the governors are willing to see offshore oil and gas developed rationally, in a way that will protect the citizens of our states and of the United States. We want to see an optimum result for the best interests of all our people. We are not obstructionists, only realists.

MAYOR BRADLEY: Thank you very much, Governor Byrne. Mr. Haynes, would you take up on this issue, perhaps from a different point of view?

MR. HAYNES: Discussions of the subject of offshore drilling have, to say the least, become somewhat emotional and more than somewhat confusing. The fact is that this nation is consuming more oil than it is producing: in 1950 we were importing practically no oil from foreign sources, while this year we will probably be dependent on foreign sources for 40 percent of our oil requirements, and unless something is done, by 1977 or 1978 we will be importing perhaps 50 percent of our oil requirements.

I was reading an article in one of the major newspapers the other day, and two points mentioned in the article struck me as quite pertinent. One is that this nation is spending as much money today on imported oil as it was spending on the Vietnam War at its peak. The second was that if we were to undergo another embargo such as the one that occurred in the winter of 1973–74, it could mean the loss of 2 million jobs in this country and could affect our gross national product by some $50 to $80 billion. I think that everyone on this panel will agree that, given those facts, we should get on with some kind of a program to minimize our dependence on foreign sources of energy. I think everyone will agree to that.

Now, there is no question that our country has an abundance of alternate energy resources. Certainly we have an abundance of coal; we have the potential to expand our nuclear generating capacity; we have the potential to gasify coal and to liquefy coal; we have tremendous shale oil resources. Certainly the development of all of these alternate resources should be pursued, and the oil industry is willing to play its part in the development of these alternate resources, but the industry—like all of us—needs an agreed-upon national energy program that will provide a stable economic and political climate within which to get this job done.

Having said that, I think I should point out that in my judgment all these alternate energy resources will not play a substantial role in solving our energy problem, certainly not in the next decade and perhaps not for as long as fifteen years. I do not see any alternatives in the short term, in the next decade, to exploring and developing our domestic oil and gas resources. The experts in this field have made studies—the U.S. Geological Survey, the National Petroleum Council (NPC), the National Academy of Sciences (NAS)—and while the various experts differ in their estimates of our potential resources, they all believe that the greatest potential for additional oil and gas in this country lies in the outer continental shelf (OCS) and in Alaska.

I am, of course, part of the energy industry, and I think I have a responsibility to the American public to advocate what in my judgment is really the only feasible short-term solution to this problem. For me to take any other position would, I think, be totally irresponsible, and for that reason, I urge the federal government and the states to get together and work out their differences—and while they are working out their differences, let us get on with exploring for oil offshore, because offshore exploration really is the only short-term solution.

Many of the people in this country think of energy as the means of getting from where they might be to where they want to go, or perhaps as turning a light on at home or something of that sort. But I would like to emphasize the fact that energy is the underpinning of our economic system—which means that energy can be equated to jobs. The offshore drilling decision is basically a political decision, but I hope that the decision makers, when they deliberate and establish priorities, will recognize that we are not just talking about inconveniences—about getting places or turning out lights—when we talk about a shortage of energy in this country. We are talking about jobs and an adverse effect on our economy.

CAPTAIN COUSTEAU: First, I am a little embarrassed to be here on this panel as a foreign citizen. My only reason for accepting the invitation is that I am paying my taxes in the United States; otherwise, I would have turned this invitation down. Also, I do spend most of my time here when I am not at sea.

MAYOR BRADLEY: You have earned your right to speak.

CAPTAIN COUSTEAU: I am very disturbed that throughout this conference, as we have discussed the costs and benefits of offshore drilling, our starting point has always been the assumption that offshore oil is definitely needed. This need has never been substantiated here by studies or figures; it has merely been assumed as an axiom. Now I am not saying that offshore drilling is not needed. I am just saying that during this conference the need has not been demonstrated.

A second thing. Looking at this problem from a double point of view, both as an ocean explorer and leader of scientists—though I am not a scientist myself—and as a man who has time to think when up on the bridge, I have reflected that everyone is talking about short-term independence, and it occurs to me that desire for short-term energy independence for this country may be more dangerous than temporary dependence and long-term independence. Let me explain what I mean.

Of course, we know and the Europeans know very well what it costs to buy energy outside. Here you buy perhaps 40 or 50 percent of your oil from abroad. In France we buy 90 percent from the Arab oil countries and the present cost is a terrible drain on our economy.

But we are in a time when international affairs are relatively at ease, even if the headlines in some papers dramatize things. It is said that things have rarely been as easy as they are now for the Western world. Certainly this is unlikely to last forever. In ten or fifteen or twenty years we may face some critical strategic situations for which easy oil energy will be required. If out of expediency we have quickly burned our last offshore reserves in time of peace and ease, we will be without any kind of resources in hard times, and we will be strangled. This possibility has formed my general approach to this problem. I know that offshore drilling is technically feasible, and that the protection of the environment can be dealt with in ways that we may talk about later on. I know that, as a temporary bridge to the future, offshore oil may be necessary. Nevertheless, it seems to me that right now we have to develop other sources of energy, especially of the renewable and nonpolluting kind, though it is likely to take enormous funding.

MR. HUGHES: It is a pleasure to have the opportunity to explain the government's position on offshore oil drilling. Our topic today is costs and benefits, and I might mention that in 1970 this country spent $3 billion for offshore oil, while last year, 1974, we spent $24 billion, which represents a significant cost to the American public. We believe that among the total array of energy sources available to us for the near term, offshore oil, as Mr. Haynes said, provides the one real additional source of domestic supply.

In this country we use about 17 million barrels of oil per day. We produce about 11 million barrels of oil a day, and our production is declining—last year it declined 8 percent, and perhaps next year it will drop by 6 percent. Certainly, over the short term, over the next ten years, there will be a significant decline in the production of domestic American petroleum. That is one of the reasons we believe that it is incumbent upon the government to ensure that we conduct an orderly program to determine where our additional resources are. Of course we are concerned about the prospect of using up our fossil fuel resources now and not having any fossil fuels to serve us later on, but we really do not believe we are planning to use up our offshore oil.

Our program right now is an orderly series of lease sales over the next four years that will permit exploration of the remaining unexplored areas of the outer continental shelf so we can find where the oil is and where it is not. We recognize that both strategic and domestic production conditions may change so as to force us to revise a given schedule. We believe the government's program has the flexibility necessary for dealing with changes in our energy situation. Even so, because of the long lead times involved in offshore drilling, we believe it is incumbent on the government and certainly on the American public to support a program that will provide us with those resources when we need them.

The government recognizes that, as the program expands from its traditional area of operation in the Gulf of Mexico, we will have to explain it carefully in the new states involved. We recognize that the program will have certain effects on the coastal areas and we are trying to come to grips with the problems that the states may face from offshore development. We have consequently made a series of changes in the program that will meet many of the objections made in the past. I think the most important change—one that I hope we can discuss in a little more detail here—is a commitment on the government's part to work more closely than before with the states. We intend to include state officials in the process by which the ultimate decision is made to lease or not to lease.

We want to continue working on our system to see whether there are additional changes that could make it better. There is a great national debate now on Capitol Hill as to what will ultimately be the national energy policy. As that debate goes on, we must continue to work on the outer continental shelf program. We do not see any other source of petroleum in the short term. Of course, coal gasification, coal liquefaction, solar energy, and geothermal energy are all potential future energy resources; but when we talk about these, we are talking about their becoming available beyond 1985 and 1990, and we need immediate relief from our short-term energy supply problem.

MAYOR BRADLEY: It seems to me that Governor Byrne is saying, "Not so fast, hold up, let's have a little more orderly process." Mr. Hughes is saying, "We think this is a reasonable process, the phasing of this program is well timed, and we want to involve the states." I did not hear him say "involve the cities," but I know he intended to. Captain Cousteau is saying, first, that we have seen no demonstrable evidence in this conference that we ought to be drilling on the outer continental shelf, and, second, that we ought to develop some alternate sources of energy right now, despite the costs. Mr. Haynes is saying that there is only a limited amount of oil available in this country and in the world, and we had better get on with our work because it will take ten or fifteen years even to bring it onshore for refining.

MR. HAYNES: May I correct a misunderstanding? I certainly did not intend to suggest there was a shortage of oil in the world. Indeed, there is a fully adequate supply of oil in the world. Our problem is with the supply of oil right here in the United States, and my view is that we should minimize our dependency on these foreign sources for the many reasons which Mr. Hughes mentioned. There is a considerable amount of oil in the world, but here in the United States we are consuming a lot more than we are producing. I think in the interests of our economy, perhaps also in the interests of our national security, it behooves us to limit our dependence on foreign sources.

Of course, there is no question that oil is in finite supply, but I want it to be clear that in the foreseeable future there is an abundance of oil in the free world. We are all aware of the fact that there are many millions of barrels a day of surplus producing capacity at the present time in the Middle East and among non-Middle Eastern OPEC countries. The supply is finite, but at least there is still quite a lot of oil for the future. Unfortunately for us as Americans, two-thirds of the oil in the free world happens to be located in the Middle East, and a larger percentage in the OPEC countries.

CAPTAIN COUSTEAU: What bothers me is that we seem to be saying that there is a lot of oil elsewhere in the world and we should burn ours quickly in the United States. Do I understand what is being said?

MR. HUGHES: I do not think it can be said that our position is to burn it quickly, since the lead time involved is substantial and the process of exploration I referred to earlier is an orderly one. From the opening of the proceedings to sale of rights takes up to two years. It takes one to three years from the time of the sale of rights to exploration, and three to eight years beyond that before development might occur, should oil be found. I would emphasize that phrase—"should oil be found"—because I believe we all keep it in mind that the oil business is a speculative one.

In any case, the operation of this system now takes years rather than months or days. If we delay now for several years in order to determine whether or not the system could be a little better, ten years from now we might find that we had started five years too late, and we might be faced with a massive change in the American lifestyle.

GOVERNOR BYRNE: The governors have been portrayed as the heavies in this debate. Perhaps we ought to clear that up a little bit with Mr. Hughes and Mr. Haynes. If the governors today suddenly withdrew every objection they had to offshore drilling, where would we be? Where would we go tomorrow?

MR. HUGHES: I think it is our intention to proceed with the orderly process that we outlined. We do not believe the governors are the heavies: after all, there are other groups besides state officials concerned about the conduct of the program. But we do think it is in the national interest to proceed with an orderly plan to develop oil resources and have them available for the American people, and we intend to proceed within the context of existing laws.

GOVERNOR BYRNE: Are we governors lousing up an orderly plan that you had and have, Mr. Hughes?

MR. HUGHES: No, I think that the governors have sharpened the debate, and that is what our system of government is all about.

GOVERNOR BYRNE: Do you have a plan that would let you go ahead tomorrow with accelerated exploration to determine where the energy resources are, and still allow an orderly decision-making process?

MR. HUGHES: It depends on what area you are talking about. If your reference is to the Atlantic, I can tell you that there we intend to resume our scheduled initial call for nominations.

GOVERNOR BYRNE: Your environmental impact statements will let you do that now?

MR. HUGHES: Not yet; the environmental impact statements are part of the process.

GOVERNOR BYRNE: I see.

MR. HUGHES: The decision to lease will not be made until all these things that you refer to are accomplished.

GOVERNOR BYRNE: The Interior Department filed an environmental impact statement in October which attempted to justify the entire speeded-up program.

MR. HUGHES: That environmental impact statement covers the entire program. For each given sale area, the department does a site-specific environmental impact statement, taking into account local environmental, social, and economic factors.

GOVERNOR BYRNE: You do not really expect anyone to believe that the environmental impact statement the department filed would justify offshore drilling today, do you?

MR. HUGHES: We think the statement justifies offshore drilling.

GOVERNOR BYRNE: That statement would justify offshore drilling?

MR. HUGHES: In an overview, covering the seventeen areas in the outer continental shelf, ranging from Alaska to the entire east-west coast and the Gulf of Mexico, the statement justifies offshore drilling.

GOVERNOR BYRNE: You had hearings on that environmental impact statement, did you not?

MR. HUGHES: That is true.

GOVERNOR BYRNE: Some were in Trenton, some here, others in Alaska and elsewhere. I did not hear of anyone in that state characterizing that environmental impact statement as being adequate to justify drilling offshore today.

MR. HUGHES: I think there were some supporters. I know it can be said that the only supporters were in the oil industry, but we believe that the offshore drilling program has a number of supporters greater than the number of persons who voiced their opposition to the program at these public hearings.

GOVERNOR BYRNE: I do not care about counting noses. I do care about whether the environmental impact statement the department has come up with so far provides an adequate basis on which to proceed. That is the question.

MR. HUGHES: If your question is whether we will make some additional changes in the statement, the answer is that we will. Nevertheless, we think that by and large the statement is an adequate document.

GOVERNOR BYRNE: You mean that you could have gotten away with that statement.

MR. HUGHES: We do not like to use that kind of language. We think the statement was prepared in good faith; and that it does in fact meet the requirements of the National Environmental Protection Act (NEPA) and the general concerns outlined in that act.

MAYOR BRADLEY: Governor Byrne, I think your reputation as a prosecutor is well earned. Let us see if we can get to our other panelists now. A common question is whether we need to proceed as quickly as we are on offshore drilling. Some observers claim that, even if we were to proceed today, we could not extract the oil, we could not bring it in, we could not refine it, in less than eight or ten years or perhaps longer.

MR. HAYNES: This question is almost always put into the form, Should we move so rapidly? I think we ought to ask ourselves instead, Should we continue to delay this process? The oil industry has been asking for accelerated leasing offshore for years. We respect the efforts of the various interested parties, the environmentalists and the states, and we have advocated for some time—we have gone on record to this effect—that there should be some mechanism whereby the coastal states could share in whatever revenue or economic benefit the federal government derives from offshore leasing. But I am concerned when the question is raised only in the form,

Should we proceed so quickly? when in fact we have been delayed almost to the point of irresponsibility. I have already said several times that there is a lot of oil in the world, and Captain Cousteau has said that since the world is relatively stable politically right now, there is no reason to think we could not continue to bring this oil in. But I would remind you of a point I made in my opening statement—we are still open to a political embargo on oil.

If the embargo is enforced again, it will not merely be an inconvenience, not merely mean long lines at service stations—though I do not like those any better than anyone else, and the lines where we live were so long that my wife read *Exodus* sitting in a service station line—not merely mean mild inconveniences of that sort, but will represent an attack on our underlying economic system. We all ought to be concerned about jobs, and indeed I think we are: for that reason, among others, I do not want to be put in the position of defending our "proceeding so quickly." Instead, I would like someone to tell me why the government has delayed our proceeding for the last two or three years, which is time we could ill afford to be delayed.

MAYOR BRADLEY: Mr. Haynes, perhaps we ought to ask Assistant Secretary Hughes about the delay, because those who serve at the state and city level, and those who are described as environmentalists, really had this debate on offshore drilling sharpened in the course of the last year, when the program and the environmental impact statement were thrust upon them in the latter part of 1974 with only a few weeks given them to respond to it. Perhaps if that environmental impact statement had been prepared years ago, and the states, cities, and environmentalists had been given the chance to evaluate it carefully, we would now be at a point where we could say this is a clear and justified decision. Even now the cities and states are being told this is a clear and justified decision, though the department acknowledges that it will have to make some changes in the initial statement. Apparently the department wants to proceed with the site-specific environmental impact statements even before there is a change in its earlier impact statement.

MR. HUGHES: That is correct. Now, I think I might first address the question, Why the delay? I think all of us through the 1950s and 1960s went merrily on our way, trying to avoid hard decisions on energy, assuming there would never be a problem with the U.S. energy supply. Perhaps, in hindsight, that was a bad way to go, but it tended to be the way in which government went at all levels. What sharpened the issue in everybody's mind was the change in the price of foreign oil from $3.50 to $11.00 or $12.00 a barrel, a change which caused energy costs throughout the country to skyrocket and produced massive disruption. The government responded to the disruption and the skyrocketing prices with an attempt to accelerate the program through an orderly legal process. Admittedly, we do wish to accelerate the program.

As for the relation of the environmental impact statement on the government's overall accelerated program to the various site-specific statements, and particularly the one for southern California, we believe that it is in the national interest for us to complete the final statements at all levels as rapidly as possible. There is no attempt to do any business in a closet. We recognize that if the final decision on the California lease sale is to be reached, we will have to work up to that decision with a particular process oriented only towards southern California—which is why we have issued a site-specific statement for southern California, and why we intend to hold public hearings in southern California in the near term. We do not think we should be held back from these hearings because we are revising our overall statement.

The decision that is most critical is the decision to hold the sale, not the decision to issue a call for nominations, and not the decision to issue an environmental impact statement in a site-specific sense. I recognize we have an honest disagreement on the question whether state and local governments have had ample opportunity to examine the program. In many cases that issue comes down to a traditional states' rights or local rights concern.

GOVERNOR BYRNE: Is Mr. Haynes suggesting that, for instance, we should have explored and developed the Baltimore Canyon trough off New Jersey years ago?

MR. HAYNES: Governor, to be perfectly honest, I did not learn of the exploration potential of the Baltimore Canyon until just a few years ago. Certainly I know our geologists had been looking up and down the East Coast, and I am sure all of our competitors' geologists had been looking up and down the East Coast, just as they have been looking all over the world; but the Baltimore Canyon became a "household word" in the oil industry only a short time back.

GOVERNOR BYRNE: I am not criticizing anyone and I know that, as a matter of fact, it would have been economically unfeasible to develop the Baltimore Canyon trough as recently as a few years ago.

MR. HAYNES: It probably would have. And I would like to make it clear that when we say "to develop the Baltimore Canyon," we realize that we do not know whether there is a teacup full of oil in the Baltimore Canyon. There may not be enough oil to fill a glass. What we are talking about is the potential for oil, and unless we get on with this program, we will not know whether there is oil out there at all.

GOVERNOR BYRNE: I would like to make one thing clear. I believe there has been an organized campaign by the oil companies to talk unrealistically about jobs

136

and to make it appear that anyone who wants the orderly development of the Baltimore Canyon trough or any other offshore area is opposed to the preserving of jobs in the United States. I think that appearance is absolutely misleading. If Mr. Haynes would answer a few questions—such as when we should have explored and developed the Baltimore Canyon and what the oil industry has against the orderly development of the Baltimore Canyon or any other area with the potential of offshore oil and gas resources—we will be able to put the whole issue in perspective.

MR. HAYNES: May I answer those questions? First of all, Governor Byrne says that the idea of relating energy to jobs is part of an organized campaign, but I think this is the first time I have ever spoken on the subject publicly. I can assure you my remarks are not part of any campaign as far as I am concerned: I happen to believe very strongly that jobs and energy are related. Secondly, we have been talking about developing the Baltimore Canyon. Now my remarks a moment ago had to do with the general subject of offshore exploration. We are talking not only about the potential for exploration off the New Jersey coast, but also about potential for exploration all up and down the East Coast. We are talking about the Gulf of Alaska. We are talking about southern California. We are talking about every bit of the United States's outer continental shelf where there appears to be any potential for oil and gas. We are not directing our attention only to the Baltimore Canyon, and I am not suggesting that anybody is to be criticized for not having gotten on with the Baltimore Canyon. All I am saying is that various groups have emitted a certain amount of criticism against the federal government for proceeding too rapidly, but that, in fact, the government has delayed too long. I can cite what the oil industry kept telling the public and the government about natural gas back in the 1950s. I do not wish to deal in hindsight, but I might like to say we told you so—we were talking about these problems as early as 1952 and 1953, and the problems we saw then have borne fruit. There is a shortage of natural gas in this country. It is serious, and it affects Governor Byrne's state among others.

GOVERNOR BYRNE: We do not mind criticizing the federal government. We do it all the time. But as it happens we are now criticizing the federal government's policy on the shut-in gas and oil wells that some of the oil companies may have.

MR. HAYNES: I am not criticizing the federal government alone. I am very much aware that one thing that has impeded accelerated offshore leasing has been industry accidents. Those accidents were very much to be regretted, and I think the industry has regretted them more than anyone else.

GOVERNOR BYRNE: You have improved your technology since Santa Barbara, I trust.

MR. HAYNES: There is no question that the oil industry has improved its technology, and the government has improved its operating requirements.

GOVERNOR BYRNE: All of this has been for the good.

MR. HAYNES: Yes, this has been for the good. But I would like to get back to the question of these accidents for just a moment. I think four accidents on 18,000 wells is a pretty good record, though of course it is not perfect, and we cannot guarantee a perfect performance in the years to come. But I would say to Governor Byrne that we all took a risk even in getting out of bed this morning: we cannot live without risk. I submit that the risk of offshore drilling is an acceptable risk. If I am criticizing the government, it is because I wish the federal government and the states and the cities would get together and get on with the solution to this problem. We have been talking about an energy program for months and months and months, and we do not have an energy program. In the meantime, this country has an energy problem, and the oil industry would be irresponsible if it did not treat these matters as vital.

GOVERNOR BYRNE: Mr. Hughes will tell you that we have been getting together.

MR. HAYNES: If we can be of any help, we would be delighted.

MAYOR BRADLEY: May I ask for a comment by Captain Cousteau on these accidents, as you call them—on the harm to the sea and onshore. I think you are as familiar with these areas as anyone. What is your judgment?

CAPTAIN COUSTEAU: It is obvious that an oil spill is a disaster. Nevertheless, the record of the industry shows that a lot more damage has been done by the transportation of oil than by drilling. Recently, to take just two examples, spills from two supertankers, one around the Cape of Good Hope and one in the Chilean Channel on the southern tip of South America, spread devastation over a big area. Transportation is responsible for a lot more trouble than offshore oil drilling: there is no question about that. Nevertheless, an oil spill in a well that is not far away from shore, though a local and temporary disaster, is a disaster nonetheless. My principal worry is that for the oil industry, as well as for nuclear plants, those very ones who may endanger public safety or the environment are the only ones who have the right to control and assess what they are doing and how they are doing it. The oil industry is controlling its own safety—the atomic energy industry is controlling its own safety—and apparently no one else has the right to investigate. I would strongly recommend that if offshore drilling is to take place an independent agency be commissioned to control the safety measures.

138

MR. HUGHES: Mayor Bradley, I think it might be appropriate for me to respond at this point. I would certainly take exception to Captain Cousteau's remarks since the federal government does, in fact, control the industry.

CAPTAIN COUSTEAU: The Department of the Interior is not an independent agency.

MR. HUGHES: It is independent of the oil industry.

CAPTAIN COUSTEAU: Not so much. The department and the industry have the same interests. I believe some more independent group, such as the National Academy of Sciences, should commission a neutral organization to control the oil industry's safety measures in offshore drilling.

MR. HUGHES: Since the Santa Barbara spill, the federal government has made a number of changes in the operation of the offshore program. The number of inspectors has increased almost tenfold. The number of operating orders and safety requirements to which the companies are required to adhere has been considerably increased and the cost of safety to the industry has certainly escalated. Additional research has been accomplished in the area of spill containment and in many of the other areas associated with potential spills.

We recognize that there may always be an accident, so long as humans are involved in the oil industry or any other industry, but we think that probability is small at this point. We think that of the two alternatives, massive tanker traffic or increased offshore operation, offshore operation certainly has less potential for damage.

MAYOR BRADLEY: Mr. Assistant Secretary, do you believe that there is a minimal possibility of damage from oil drilling? Is the Department of the Interior willing to set up some kind of a liability procedure to protect those who may be damaged if, in fact, a spill occurs?

MR. HUGHES: Yes. As a matter of fact, within the administration we are now trying to set up the final wording of an unlimited liability bill which would establish a front-end fund so that if a community were subject to an oil spill—and we certainly hope this never comes about—there would be money available immediately to meet the disaster, to help that community pull itself back together. We think the climate in the Congress is certainly going to be very good for an unlimited liability bill. As I am sure all of us are aware, Congress is debating several other issues related to the outer continental shelf program. But this is one that we in the Department of the Interior strongly support. There will be a debate over the actual numbers involved, but it certainly makes good sense from our standpoint to establish the fund.

MAYOR BRADLEY: Do you think it is appropriate that the program be continued on its schedule before these decisions are made?

MR. HUGHES: We think it is appropriate for the program to be continued. In the next four to eight weeks, the Congress will probably come to some decision on general changes in the OCS program. We hope the Congress will take up the issue of an unlimited liability bill this term. Because of the time frames involved, even if we should have a sale in southern California in the early fall of 1975, it would probably be at least another year to three years before anything occurred in the way of drilling, so we believe there is ample time for such a provision to be enacted. If we waited until each of the concerns in the immediate OCS program were resolved and until we had buttoned down our national energy policy, it might be several years, which we believe would not be in the national interest.

CAPTAIN COUSTEAU: I have a major objection to this. Unlimited liability compensation would encourage irresponsibility. The safety measures would be much stronger if they were taken in advance of a spill. We always see the same kind of attitude: we prefer to clean the water when it is dirty than to avoid dirtying the water; we want to repair the damage done on the coast after it is done, instead of avoiding doing the damage. It is always the same.

Now there was something concerning liability that shocked me during the discussions yesterday. The question was raised, At what are you going to value the lives of birds? We discussed at length whether it was $1.00 or $10.00. That is nonsense. The life of a bird is invaluable—it is something that is precious in itself and that cannot be tagged with a price in dollars.

MR. HUGHES: I think it might be appropriate to ask Mr. Haynes to give us some idea what changes have been made in the way of oil industry safety since Santa Barbara. I know considerable changes have been made: the industry has not stood still technologically, and government awareness on this issue has certainly increased.

MR. HAYNES: I do not think time would permit me to enumerate all the things that have happened. I believe we should give the government a great deal of credit in this area. A little earlier Mr. Hughes mentioned the additional number of inspectors required and so forth, and I started to interrupt him and say that the number of reports we have to file has multiplied about a millionfold. Though I believe that is all to the good in its final effect. I am delighted to have a chance to say something pleasant about the government because it may be thought that I have been criticizing the government too much.

The oil industry has improved our technology as Mr. Hughes notes. We have spent millions—

CAPTAIN COUSTEAU: You see? . . . Hand in hand.

MR. HAYNES: —I would hate to think we were not operating in concert, Captain Cousteau.

CAPTAIN COUSTEAU: I would like you to operate in concert with the public, too.

MR. HAYNES: We are certainly trying to do that. We are working with the government and I have always thought that the government was representative of the public.

CAPTAIN COUSTEAU: Through a complicated system.

MR. HAYNES: Be that as it may, not to belabor this point, we have improved our training, we have spent millions in research and development, we have formed cooperatives to handle emergencies when they exist—thank goodness the cooperative in San Francisco has been called on only once or twice, most recently by the Coast Guard. We have made great strides, but I do not want to take the time to elaborate on all of them. Obviously we are spending a lot of money in research and development for our drilling techniques and platform designs. We are working on underwater completion. We are doing a lot in this area.

CAPTAIN COUSTEAU: Would you be against the National Academy of Sciences' looking into it?

MR. HAYNES: Captain Cousteau, I would not be against that.

CAPTAIN COUSTEAU: No?

MR. HAYNES: As a matter of fact, I think that when the government lays down regulations, operating restrictions, and so on, they would seek counsel and advice.

CAPTAIN COUSTEAU: Yes, and why not from the National Academy of Sciences?

MR. HAYNES: I think that is a fine idea. We would not have any objection to that.

MR. HUGHES: We certainly have invited outside sources to provide input into the program.

CAPTAIN COUSTEAU: And why not the National Academy of Sciences, which is the highest authority in this field?

MR. HUGHES: What would be their exact function?

CAPTAIN COUSTEAU: To name the experts, to control the reports, and to give their advice to the government.

MR. HUGHES: The academy does of course give advice to the government. Is your proposal for the academy to review the program?

CAPTAIN COUSTEAU: No. To review safety—only safety. That is all.

MR. HUGHES: I think I would be opposed to asking the academy to undertake an operational program of safety and inspection, in part because it would be subject to the same sort of criticism to which you are subjecting the federal government.

CAPTAIN COUSTEAU: Why?

MR. HUGHES: Why not? We have scientists who work in our department, too. Do you mean to imply that the academy would have scientists who are a little more objective?

CAPTAIN COUSTEAU: A little more independent, yes.

MR. HUGHES: But where does the National Academy of Sciences obtain its funding?

CAPTAIN COUSTEAU: From various sources—not only from the government.

GOVERNOR BYRNE: May I ask a question? The suggestion has been made that we have an either-or situation—either supertankers or offshore drilling. Mr. Haynes, is that so? Would offshore resources eliminate the need for the supertanker?

MR. HAYNES: I think the easiest way to answer that question is to say that if we do not get on with offshore exploration and find some oil, and (I might add) produce it, then we are going to be more dependent upon foreign sources. Now, there is no other way to get foreign oil into this country than by tankers. There is at present no way to bring a supertanker—VLCC (Very Large Crude Carrier)— the so-called 200,000-ton class and above—into the United States, because we do not have a port facility to accommodate one. I think it is horrendous that we do not, because it means that the consuming public is paying a premium for transporting oil in smaller tankers. To answer the governor's question, we can say that if we import more oil, the only way to get it here is in tankers, and a lack of offshore drilling will increase the tanker traffic. I do not think our debate should be on the advantages of VLCCs as against small tankers.

GOVERNOR BYRNE: I did not want to make that the issue. I just wanted to make sure whether you think we are in an either-or situation.

MR. HAYNES: I do not think there is any question that we are going to have additional tanker traffic to this country.

GOVERNOR BYRNE: In any event?

MR. HAYNES: It is the only way to get foreign oil here.

GOVERNOR BYRNE: In any event?

MR. HAYNES: No. Obviously, to the extent that we can find and develop oil offshore, that oil will displace imports.

CAPTAIN COUSTEAU: For a few years?

MR. HAYNES: Well, until we can get into some of these alternate sources of energy.

CAPTAIN COUSTEAU: But we have not tried. We have not tried.

MR. HAYNES: Pardon?

CAPTAIN COUSTEAU: That is my entire point today. We would very much support the temporary bridge of offshore oil drilling if it were a bridge to a monumental program for alternate nonpollutant sources, but such a program does not exist.

MR. HUGHES: Captain Cousteau, I think the government does have programs for alternate sources.

CAPTAIN COUSTEAU: Yes, but I happen to know that the programs are ridiculously small when compared to the amount of investment that is necessary. I have all the information here. We need a total of about $1 trillion in fifteen to twenty years. This, of course, is not to be paid for by the federal government alone; it has to be paid for by the economy as a whole. If such a program is not adopted, what then? The program of offshore drilling is just a temporary oxygen tent before we suffocate from lack of energy at the mercy of the foreign producers. That is exactly what is going to happen in twenty years.

MR. HAYNES: Captain Cousteau, the oil industry certainly supports a massive research and development program.

CAPTAIN COUSTEAU: I am not concerned with the oil industry's program.

MR. HAYNES: I know that. I just want to have it on record here that we support a massive research and development program in this area.

CAPTAIN COUSTEAU: Yes, I know.

MR. HAYNES: So far as my company is concerned—I cannot speak for the whole industry, but I am confident that others are doing the same thing—we are spending sizeable sums on research and development in coal gasification, coal liquefaction, shale oil development, solar energy, geothermal energy, and things of that nature. It will still be ten or fifteen years before those sources become available to us.

CAPTAIN COUSTEAU: Fifteen to twenty years.

MR. HAYNES: I might add that the cost of these alternate sources of energy are nowhere near the figure that is being bandied about in the press and in Washington. But I can assure you that at $6.00 or $7.00 a barrel—and I am talking about 1975 dollars—there is not going to be a lot of shale oil development or coal liquefaction or coal gasification or tar sand development. It just would not be economically feasible, because the costs would be in excess of $14.00 to $15.00 a barrel.

CAPTAIN COUSTEAU: I am sorry.

MR. HAYNES: That is not to say we should not go into these things.

CAPTAIN COUSTEAU: No.

MR. HAYNES: But I think we should recognize that it is not going to be cheap.

CAPTAIN COUSTEAU: And these alternate sources of energy that are the only major ones now really being considered in the national program—such as coal gasification and to a lesser degree tar sands and shale oil—are either potentially heavily polluting sources of energy or land-destroying sources of energy. The only sources of energy that are absolutely pollution-free and are in a tremendous abundance in this country—geothermal and solar—are considered as utopian.

MR. HAYNES: I hope not, because we are doing some work in those areas right now.

CAPTAIN COUSTEAU: You largely said that yourself—that if you do not have the appropriate support from the authorities, they are utopian. The federal government must turn its program to nonpolluting renewable sources of energy. If it did so, I do not think there is one environmentalist who would not support a program of offshore drilling.

MAYOR BRADLEY: Mr. Hughes has said that the government does have a program and is proposing to spend money or is spending money in this kind of research.

MR. HUGHES: Right.

MAYOR BRADLEY: Perhaps he can quickly tell us how much.

MR. HUGHES: I think Captain Cousteau disputes the figure, but it my understanding that the 1976 federal budget contains $53 million for solar energy research. We are also spending—

CAPTAIN COUSTEAU: That includes all forms of solar energy?

MR. HUGHES: That is correct. In addition, we are spending tens of millions of dollars in other fossil fuel research on the problems of coal gasification and liquefaction. We are certainly continuing to explore and experiment with geothermal resources. It is the opinion of our experts at this time that geothermal energy will never supply much more than a very small amount of the energy requirements of this country. But we are not giving up on it as an alternate source of energy.

MAYOR BRADLEY: One other question. Since there seems to be some suspicion of any other research group, whether it is government or industry, what would be the position of the Department of the Interior on the National Academy of Sciences' conducting the review of the program and making a report?

MR. HUGHES: We still have that question under advisement. We are not willing to make a commitment at this point to have such a study conducted if we have to suspend all activities in the program for some period of time, something that is normally implicit in the suggestion that the National Academy of Sciences carry out the review. We are certainly continuing to work with organizations like the National Governors Conference on the idea of a third-party shoreside impact study that would not be suspect because the Department of the Interior or indeed any federal agency had done it. Our basic intention is to conduct the orderly program laid out in our tentative schedule and get these answers along the way, rather than stopping everything now and waiting one to five years before resuming a program that requires a five-year lead time.

MAYOR BRADLEY: Thank you very much, gentlemen, for the illuminating discussion. And now we turn to questions from the audience. I should mention that the audience here includes a number of recognized experts in the field.

PROFESSOR MEAD: I have a question for Mr. Haynes. He spoke at length about the employment effects of another embargo. His point was that a second embargo would be a disaster. Then he said that the only solution—I think that was his exact wording—was offshore development. I think he might perhaps agree with me that offshore development is part of the solution, but not the only solution. I was a little concerned that there has been no discussion here about the possibility of crude oil storage inasmuch as a system of storage might be set up to provide us with one year of security or even two years. Could Mr. Haynes comment?

MR. HAYNES: When I made the comment that offshore drilling was the only solution, I think I said that it was the only medium-term or short-term solution for developing additional energy resources in this country. And I do stand by what I said. Now I did comment on the effect of an embargo. I think we may have been remiss in not addressing ourselves to strategic storage, which I think is an excellent idea. It is one, as you know, that the National Petroleum Council recommended less than a year ago, and it is one that my company wholeheartedly supports; it is part of the President's energy program, and I think it makes a lot of sense. I hope that the energy debate between the administration and the Congress will soon be resolved, and that when it is we will have strategic storage. I think strategic storage would certainly mitigate the effect of another embargo.

DON TILLINGHAST, Office of the Attorney General, State of Alaska: I have three quick questions for Mr. Hughes. First, I wish he would expand on the problems with the tanker/platform trade-off theory as it pertains to OCS operations off Alaska. Second, in regard to his discussion with Captain Cousteau on the objectivity or the lack of objectivity of regulation by the U.S. Geological Survey (USGS), I wonder why the Department of the Interior has refused to require application of the best commercially feasible technology for exploration and development, despite the recommendations of scientists, despite the recommendations of the Environmental Protection Agency (EPA), and despite the recommendations of the Council on Environmental Quality (CEQ)? Third, if the Department of the Interior is as objective as the assistant secretary says it is, then why in the Gulf of Alaska is it continuing the practice of developing operating orders in consultation with industry, even though Dr. McKelvey, the director of the USGS, promised the House Government Operations Committee it would discontinue that practice and would give

146

industry only the same role in the development of those orders as the affected states and the interested public?

MR. HUGHES: I will try to answer the three issues you raise. First, on the trade-off between platforms and tankers as it affects Alaska: I think we all understand that Alaska is a unique case. Alaska is certainly more than self-sufficient in fossil fuel resources; the state will be a net exporter to the other forty-nine states. Alaska has areas of high resource potential and several that we are interested in exploring and perhaps developing in the near term. Once those resources are located, platforms would in fact be constructed and tanker traffic would proceed from Alaska to the lower forty-eight to deliver that oil. If that was the point of the question about the trade-off, I can say that we know Alaska is a giver and not a taker of energy resources.

On the matter of the government's failure to recognize the best commercial technology and failure to require its use, I must confess that I am not acquainted specifically with the issue. I think we require a certain standard of excellence so far as the technology is concerned, but whether the cost-benefit trade-off requires the best technology is something we can explore and then inform Mr. Tillinghast or Governor Hammond.

As to our continuing to work with industry on putting operating orders together, that is something, again, that I am unaware has been a subject of great controversy. We certainly need industry input on the technology that industry is planning on using in a given area, and Alaska has a hostile climate, a climate in which new operating orders or variations of existing operating orders are going to have to be put together to ensure responsible resource development. But, again, we can be in touch with Mr. Tillinghast or the governor to confirm or deny Dr. McKelvey's commitment to a congressional committee.

MR. MEEKER: I would like to address a question related to Captain Cousteau's proposal both to Captain Cousteau and to Mr. Hughes. I would like to ask Captain Cousteau, first of all, what level of funding and effort he would consider appropriate today for pursuing the development of renewable and nonpolluting energy resources, particularly solar energy. I would like to ask Mr. Hughes whether the government takes a different view of the appropriate level and effort today and, if so, what the reasons are for its taking a different view.

CAPTAIN COUSTEAU: The answer to your question is slightly complicated, but it is substantiated by research done by several organizations in this country over several years and by Eurocean, which I chair. We have consulted with such well-known study groups as Battelle in Switzerland. Of course, the figures that I am going to give you are within 30 percent, because it is very difficult to estimate such advanced projects. In discussions of solar energy up to now, the various governments of the world—and I am not pinning this down to one government, since they all do the same thing—have diverted the question just to the heating and cooling of houses. The same thing happens when environmental problems are raised: the people divert attention from the real problems by inducing their children to pick up beer cans. The real problem is not only to make energy to heat and cool individual houses, but to have huge plants making thousands of megawatts, and for this we need huge sums of money.

Let me give a few figures. In order to make things easy to understand, let us talk in terms of megawatts rather than BTUs or watts. A large nuclear plant will produce 1,000 megawatts. At the moment, the world's consumption of energy is equivalent to the production of 17,000 nuclear plants. At an efficiency of one-ten-thousandth of one percent, we could extract from solar energy the equivalent of 76,000 nuclear plants. This country is exceptionally well located for solar energy, having both the magnificently solarized desert of Arizona and the Florida current, each of which, in different ways, indirectly concentrates solar energy in small places. One square yard of the Gulf Stream in the Florida Straits has twenty times more energy concentrated on it than one square yard in Arizona. We have there a preconcentrated—one might say prefabricated—source of energy.

What I would like to see is a commitment to build an OTE test plant of, let us say, 1,000 megawatt capacity. It would probably cost around $3 billion. And of course OTE would not be the only area of research. I think that the investment in the first year could be either by direct funding or tax rebates or city money with industry joining in: the joining in would probably be necessary because the first year's budget for geothermal and solar energy research and development together should be at least $10 billion. If developed properly, this program would probably cost almost a trillion dollars in fifteen years. This is the cost we have to face: this is the price of total independence. The United States of America could be a major exporter of energy—indeed there is no other country that could produce as much solar energy.

MR. HUGHES: I think I would have to begin by saying that it would be difficult to dispute the findings that some eminent scientists have come up with in putting that study together, but that any decision to spend massive amounts of federal money on a program like this (or any other program) must always be viewed through a cost-benefit comparison. By the way, I would like to correct a figure I used earlier: in this year's budget it is $153 million, not $53 million, for all sorts of solar energy research. Certainly this is not spending at the level that Captain Cousteau would desire; but it is the opinion of experts in the government, and, I am sure, of some of the experts in the National Academy of Sciences, that that is the best program that the government can operate for the near term. Nevertheless, we are certainly willing to look at Captain Cousteau's proposal, even though the idea of adding $10 billion for solar energy research to the country's existing budget

148

burdens, when the solar energy might not be available for many years, does not seem particularly attractive. We continue to believe that we are going to be dependent upon fossil fuels in the short term, and part of our belief stems from the calculation that the government should not spend nearly a trillion dollars for solar energy right now, though that is certainly a decision open to review every year.

CAPTAIN COUSTEAU: You just implied that I said something I never said. I never said that development of solar energy would preclude development of intermediate sources of energy. I am sorry that we are always talking about the short term, the short term, the short term. I must say, I think a large segment of the population is looking a little further.

PROFESSOR MENARD: I have a question for Assistant Secretary Hughes, who, I am afraid, is getting most of the questions here. There are several bills before the Congress proposing that the Department of the Interior undertake a program of exploration of the continental shelf—including drilling—in order to get information for policy decisions. I wonder if we could learn more about the department's position on these bills. I believe I understood him to say that the department believes there would be a delay in drilling, or in development of the shelf, if the department were to do the exploration. Could he explain why this delay would arise and how long it might be?

MR. HUGHES: Allow me to review the entire subject briefly. We have several objections to the idea that the government should directly or indirectly get into exploration.

First of all, government control of exploration implies that the government will decide where the holes are to be drilled in the search for oil. We have a major problem with that, because it would centralize decision making in the oil business either in one person or in one government agency, whereas under the present system it is decentralized among fifty or sixty companies that participate in the process.

All of us must keep in mind that the oil business is a speculative business, that the oil companies are in fact gambling each time they read their seismic information and make a decision to spend money on it. The most optimistic company in a given case will win the competitive auction and will have an opportunity to see whether its decision was correct. To reduce the number of those who analyze the information, the number of gamblers, if you will, to one group, the government, would not be in the national interest. It cannot help reducing the probability of finding oil. That is our first objection to it.

Secondly, it would require that the government absorb the front-end money required to drill holes. Drilling on the outer continental shelf will range somewhere between $1 million and $10 million per hole, depending on the type of climate where the drilling takes place. In the Gulf of Mexico the cost would probably be on the low end of the spectrum, while as we move up into the more hostile areas, such as offshore Alaska, it might be closer to $10 million per hole. The government would have to pay those front-end costs, and as the person responsible for the budget for my department, I cannot say I care much for the idea of going back to the Congress and saying, We just spent $50 million of the taxpayers' money and have fifty dry holes or twenty-five dry holes, and now I want another $50 million to drill more holes. I have the feeling there would be interminable delays in getting that additional $50 million.

Our system of government, especially when it comes to the relationship between the Congress and the executive branch, is not noted for its efficiency. As a matter of fact, the government was designed with built-in delays so there would be time for our different branches to reflect on decisions. We believe if we shifted to government exploration, there would be delays. Whether the delays would be good or bad is something we could debate but not here. The point is that we think any change that would make the government, either directly or indirectly, responsible for drilling would cause delay. We would have to decide who would make the decisions. We would probably have to create a new agency or to expand the U.S. Geological Survey to take on a new role. There would be a reluctance for whomever we made responsible to jump right in and make those decisions immediately. This would be a very proper reluctance I am sure, since there would be a substantial delay caused just by the shift-over.

All this is true, but our final and basic objection to having the government take over is that we think that private industry in this country is doing the job very well. We think we have the best oil industry in the world, and an industry adequate to handling the problem, and we see no reason to change the overall system. We have made several changes in the system; we are not saying that the program itself should be inviolate. We are proposing, for example, that there be a ban on joint bidding among major companies in order to get away from the charge that the major companies dominate the OCS program. We think the ban on joint bidding is a proper action for the government to take. I suppose that the large oil companies as a group object very strenuously to that sort of restriction, but we think it is in the public interest. But this is a change within the existing system, not a change of the system as a whole.

GOVERNOR BYRNE: Mr. Mayor, may I ask Mr. Hughes what Secretary Morton meant when on March 14 he testified in part as follows: "The National Governors Conference has called for a formal separation of the decisions to lease in the area and to allow actual development in that same area. I support the objective of the National Governors Conference proposal in principle and have asked my staff to determine the administrative steps necessary to put that policy into force without introducing undue delay in the development of the national energy resources. Our solicitor has informed me that such objectives could be accomplished."

MR. HUGHES: Secretary Morton did make that statement. We think that under existing law, the 1953 Outer Continental Shelf Lands Act, we have the legal ability to create a pause between exploration and development. We are now trying to establish what such a pause would mean to the interest on the part of the oil companies in investing massive amounts of money, time, and effort in the research they undertake before they offer bids on the OCS.

GOVERNOR BYRNE: Does this testimony commit the secretary to that concept?

MR. HUGHES: Yes, in a sense, it does commit the department to finding a way to create the pause. We do not subscribe to the idea that the government should conduct the explorations, and we think we can accomplish the same goal that you and other governors want to accomplish through existing law.

MAYOR BRADLEY: In further response to Dr. Menard's question, Mr. Haynes wants to make a comment from the industry's point of view.

MR. HAYNES: I am delighted to hear the assistant secretary observe that he believed the federal government should not become involved in oil exploration. I want to commend him for that decision, because I happen to agree with it whole-heartedly for the reasons he mentioned and perhaps one or two more. Perhaps I am a little bit old-fashioned, but my basic view of government is that government should do for the people what the people are not capable of doing for themselves— if it should be done at all. To me, that is fundamental—so fundamental that it may sound trite.

In all humility, I think the oil industry over the past several years has done a very commendable job in bringing an abundance of energy at a reasonable cost to the developed and developing countries of this world. I think that getting the federal government into oil exploration would be an absolute disaster. I think it would delay offshore development for years and years.

Now, though I do not really believe that the advocates of the government's becoming involved entirely mean what they say, if we were to take some of their statements literally, we would find that they are suggesting the government explore for oil, make an absolute determination as to the amount of oil that is in a particular basin, and then open the basin up for bidding. In other words, the industry would in effect be buying fuel oil in the tank. I would like to remind anyone who is interested in this subject that the Gulf of Mexico is one of the most prolific oil-producing basins in the United States. We have been producing oil there for twenty-five to thirty years, and we are still exploring for oil in that particular area. If the statements are taken literally, these advocates of government involvement suggest the U.S. government spend twenty-five years determining how much oil is in an area before it decides to develop it. Of course, they cannot really mean what they say, but I think this is a point we must consider. Even for a given structure,

151

a given salt dome or whatever geologic configuration there may be, we do not define in absolute terms the total reserves until we have drilled a few exploratory holes, a few delineation holes, until we have installed some platforms, until we have drilled development wells, and have obtained some production history. Even then we find oil years later in deeper horizons. Now, I am not trying to confuse this issue with details. I want to be sure that people understand that, if we were going to separate exploration from production or development, we would have to be very careful how we defined exploration and production.

Furthermore, if anyone really believes that the federal government could do a better job than private industry, I would like to commend to them a very quick look at who has found oil in the free world. Basically, it is the international U.S. oil industry that has found oil. There are a number of national oil companies all over the world, and with the possible exception of what the Mexican oil company found just a few months ago (after looking for some twenty-five years, I might add) and possible success by the Petrabra Company in Brazil very recently (I might add after a long effort), the world's national oil companies have not found enough oil to fill a glass. I think this reminder is needed so that we will keep the matter in the proper context.

I want to fall back to my original point. The oil industry has done a commendable job. We have made some mistakes. We regret the mistakes. We have a lot to be proud of, and I submit we can continue to do this job better than the government could do it. If anyone questions that, I would tell them to look at the postal system or Amtrak, to take just two examples.

GOVERNOR BYRNE: May I ask, if the industry is so anxious to keep the government out of this, why it is also so anxious to take tax write-offs on dry holes?

MR. HAYNES: My firm—like others—happens to be a business organization, and we have some 280,000 stockholders who have invested about $8 billion in our company.

GOVERNOR BYRNE: My only point is you are involving the government at least in your failures.

MR. HAYNES: We are involving the government the same way as the man down the street who has a factory and depreciates his plant and equipment. We are a profit-making organization: we have the incentive to make profits and if the government will give us the economic and political climate, we can get the job done.

RICHARD SNODY, National Management Association: I noticed in Governor Byrne's opening statement that he seems to be somewhat disenchanted with the fact that the offshore resources would be divided up and handed to the highest bidder. What alternative means of exploration can he offer?

GOVERNOR BYRNE: I do not know why Mr. Hughes or Mr. Morton divided the offshore oil leases into such huge blocks. I do not understand where they got the number of blocks, how they got it, and how they justify it. Second, I am not sure yet how they are going to price those leases. I would be strongly in favor of a pricing system that did not "front load" those leases with huge bonus bids; I would much prefer a system that required a minimum commitment at the beginning and a higher commitment in the royalties during production. I think Senator Bentsen of Texas has a bill that would go a long way toward doing that, so that other companies and even the states might—on their own—join in bidding for those leases, do the exploration, and make the judgments as they went along. My main reservation is this huge financial commitment at the "front end" of the current leasing/exploration/development system; there are many alternatives to that.

MR. REILLY: I think a good deal of the concern about offshore oil involves the onshore impact. In the environmental impact statement issued last year on the offshore program, about 20 out of some 2,000 pages were devoted to onshore effects. But we have just completed a study of the onshore effects in Scotland. We discovered that they are considerable—tank storage farms, refinery construction, pipelines, production, rigs, and all the rest of the things and activities that go with them.

Now, earlier this year the Department of the Interior proposed legislation to site energy facilities, in some instances over and against the wishes of state and local governments. My question is, What is going on in the department that would reassure people like Governor Byrne and the mayors as to the thought that is being put into the serious onshore problems of offshore oil and gas development and would cause them to want to give the department this authority?

MR. HUGHES: We would certainly admit that the department's role in the onshore impact question has changed over the last year to eighteen months, as we have thought in more detail about the potential impact on states other than our traditional Gulf Coast areas, where the program has operated for twenty-five years. As I mentioned, within the department we are now engaged in a dialogue with the National Governors Conference staff on what third-party entity might be able to conduct an objective study on potential onshore effects. I think all of us should keep in mind the fact that the onshore impact would vary with the locality. For example, the tiny village of Yakutat on the Gulf of Alaska has 400 people and would look forward to perhaps several thousand people coming in over a short time, should a decision be made to have a sale, and large amounts of oil be found in the gulf. Needless to say, the state of Alaska would have a then tremendous problem in establishing basic infrastructure, roads, schools, sewage systems, and so on.

The impact in southern California would certainly differ from the impact in Yakutat, and the impact in New Jersey and other East Coast states would be still

153

different. We are not trying to minimize the importance of the onshore impact from offshore development. In fact, we are trying to get a better data base upon which to encourage some changes in the system. I think the press has reported that we in the department have been reviewing revenue-sharing options, which might provide other sources of financial support to the states; but there are a lot of unknowns in the process. We hope that by working together with the states and perhaps with the National Academy of Sciences—which may be the body that we ask to do this study—we can get some outside expertise on a very complex problem. But we do not think the matter of shoreside impact is serious enough to lead us to stop the entire program for two or three years. We think there will be enough time in the course of the program to review the problem and see what we need to do to help mitigate potential adverse effects.

JOSEPH EDMONSTON, Sierra Club: The Standard Oil Company of California has been asking for a supertanker port near the Morro Bay estuary, and has also been supporting OCS drilling in southern California. This has led some people to question whether we really will have a trade-off between tanker imports and OCS development. I read several days ago an analysis suggesting that what the oil companies are trying to do is develop the OCS and tanker imports to the extent that they can then justify sending North Slope Alaska oil to Japan. I would like Mr. Haynes to comment on that, please.

MR. HAYNES: I would be delighted to comment on that. Let me take the last part of your question first, if I may. Our company has not been as successful in its exploration activity on the North Slope as our competitors have been in theirs, and I envy them. The fact is that we do not have enough production on the North Slope, or will not have enough production out of the Prudhoe Bay complex, to export anywhere except to our refineries in California. I think that the fact that we are talking about a superport up near Estero and about the OCS and that we do not have any Alaskan oil export probably answers your question. I think the industry has made it abundantly clear in the press and otherwise that it has no intention of exporting Alaskan oil to Japan or anywhere else except to the West Coast of the United States.

Now, not only have we talked about a superport in California, but we are also part of a project to build a superport off the coast of southern Louisiana. The industry is also involved in trying to put together a superport complex off Texas. There is also some discussion about offshore Mississippi. There is also some discussion about the East Coast, though I have forgotten the exact locations. All this superport construction is in the interest of trying to bring oil to the American consuming public at the least possible cost, because the economies provided by shipping oil in these large tankers is significant and would be reflected in the cost to the consuming public.

154

I do not think our position here is inconsistent at all with our desire to get on with exploration on the outer continental shelf, because if we were to develop the oil there, we would minimize our dependency on foreign sources of energy for the next decade or two, but we would still be importing. I think it behooves us to import in the most efficient manner.

MS. HELLER: I would like to address two questions to Mr. Hughes and Mr. Haynes and perhaps get Governor Byrne's reaction to their answers.

Mr. Haynes stated earlier that the industry has been asking for accelerated leasing for years. However, in the most recent lease sale in the Gulf of Mexico last month, out of all the tracts that were offered, the industry bid on less than 30 percent. There are well-documented and generally agreed-upon shortages of capital, labor, and drilling equipment in the industry. These shortages have been reported by the trade journals and *Offshore Magazine*, as well as by the Federal Energy Administration. The question is, How is the industry going to cope with accelerated leasing?

Mr. Hughes spoke about the orderly process which the department has been pursuing on OCS development. This process, however orderly it is now, has come about after very vigorous public opposition and, I think he will admit, in reaction to opposition from the governors as well as from citizen groups. I would be interested in knowing how the department is now trying to involve the public and the states in the decision process. They have issued proposed operating orders for the Gulf of Alaska which were published in the *Federal Register* about a month ago. Yet the material on which operating orders are supposed to be based has not yet come out in the environmental impact statement for that area. It seems to me that is not an example of involving the public in planned development.

MR. HAYNES: I think the thrust of your first question was that on the one hand we are advocating offshore leasing and on the other hand industry only bid on 30 percent of the leases offered in offshore Texas a few weeks ago, and that appears to be inconsistent. I think the only way I can answer that point is to say that the oil industry, of course, is a risk-taking but also a profit-making enterprise. Certain areas are put up for bids. Various companies nominate certain tracts, and the government decides which tracts are put up for bids and which are not. We have a certain amount of seismic and other information which we have acquired through our own efforts. We sit down and make the best judgment we possibly can as to the potential of a particular block. It so happened that we only bid on a few blocks, because we thought those were the only blocks that had a potential that would justify our investment and our efforts. After all, justifying investment is the name of the game. I can only conclude that the rest of the industry looked at it exactly the same way, and that therefore a number of these blocks were not bid on. Incidentally, a lot of this area was one in which very little activity has taken place in the past.

I would like to remind you that offshore in the gulf in 1974 the oil industry bid about $2.48 billion on leases in excess of the second high bid. I make that point only to suggest that the bidding process is of some economic value to the federal government. As a matter of fact, since about 1958 the oil industry has spent $60 billion offshore. The government has derived $15 billion from the industry, and the industry has a gross income of just about $15 billion. We are a long way from breaking even. But I repeat that, if the government will put up the blocks that have exploration potential, the industry will assess the risk and the possible gain, and we will get in there and play the game, and find some oil, too.

MR. HUGHES: To answer the second part of your question, we do not think it is fair to characterize our program as being created in response to public pressures. An orderly program has been in existence for many years now. We admit we are making some modifications to the program, and we are making a deliberate attempt to work more closely with governors and mayors who are involved because of the concerns of their constituents about offshore development in areas where it has never occurred. We believe that the system has needed some modifications and we have adjusted our programs in an attempt to meet the concerns of the states and the people of the country. But the actual leasing process is pretty much the same as it has been. We believe that public involvement, either directly or through public hearings, is an important vehicle for the department as well as the rest of the federal government to gain input into the program, and we also think increased cooperation with the states is important.

Secretary Morton said in his meetings with Governor Byrne and his fellow East Coast governors in January 1975 that he would invite the governors to look at the final decision document on whether to have a sale. That would certainly be a step forward in the government's opening its process to the public. A governor is the public at large or the public as represented by state and local officials. On the matter of our OCS orders for Alaska being published before the environmental impact statement is written, I do not have a solid answer except that ours is a dynamic system. We certainly do not mean to imply that there will not be more OCS orders if something new and unusual is found through environmental impact analysis in Alaska. But we need to get things done in an orderly fashion. If we wait until everyone's objection to the program, no matter how small, is taken care of, then the process will be stalled for a long time, and we do not believe that would be in the public interest.

GOVERNOR BYRNE: We do not call it pressure: we call it discussion. I appreciate Secretary Morton's having had the discussions with us. And he did say in his testimony before the Congress on March 14 that it was as a result of our discussions that he invited the governors to participate in the evaluation of the environmental impact of offshore oil. I have often said that I appreciate the willingness of Secretary Morton and of Mr. Hughes to have these discussions with us, to learn our views firsthand, and to consider our suggestions.

MR. CAHN: My question is for both Assistant Secretary Hughes and Captain Cousteau. We heard in the discussion that we need offshore oil immediately. Captain Cousteau said that if we use offshore oil up now in a time of peace, we might not have it in a time when it was needed strategically. I want to ask the question, What is our responsibility to future generations for using up this immense source of oil in fifteen to twenty years, when we do not know whether there will be other sources of energy available that could be beneficial, or not harmful, to people? A related question is, What is the government's policy on intense conservation of energy, which may be the solution to the problem of our doubling the rate of use every few years and so using energy up rapidly?

CAPTAIN COUSTEAU: I must insist that I said that I was against using up this oil if the question of replacement were not studied at the same time, because otherwise the sacrifice of the offshore oil would be useless. But if the appropriate research and development were carried out, I would support offshore development, because I think we do need to use offshore oil, provided we have a replacement for the future. Let me make that clear. This is a constructive approach. It is not a negative approach.

MR. HUGHES: I think we recognize that a decision could be made to save our additional domestic resources in the short term for some future generation, but that seems to present us with the prospect of massive dislocation and disruption in our present economy. If, in fact, we decided that we want to use half the energy next year that we used this year, that could be accomplished: we can in fact do almost anything we want in this country, but there will be a cost. We think it is in the national interest to proceed in an orderly fashion to make domestic resources available over a period of time for the needs of the nation, hoping that our research programs over the long term on fossil fuel gasification and liquefaction and the more exotic forms of energy supply such as geothermal, solar, and nuclear will produce energy that will come on line to take up most of the burden as we reach the year 2000. But that decision could be changed. The Congress in its wisdom could make a decision that we would not proceed with offshore development for some period of time, although there would be a definite price for that decision. We believe that the program the federal government is pursuing now in cooperation with other levels of government is the right program, but of course any decision in our society is open to question.

On the matter of conservation, I would say that since last year we have taken about a million barrels a day out of the consumption patterns in this country, and that, unless we go to legislated items like those proposed in the President's energy package—such as tax rebates for insulation and other monetary incentives for conservation—we will not get much more in the way of voluntary conservation. If we get into mandatory conservation, saying for example that the people can no longer have electric houses but must use some other source of energy, we have the prospect of a massive dislocation of the economy. Certainly we are open to suggestions, and the administration is continuing to review with the Congress several variations on a national energy plan that would try to bring more conservation into the picture. But conservation alone cannot solve the problem. Those who would say that we can simply decide we are not going to have any increase in energy consumption have not been talking to the American public.

CAPTAIN COUSTEAU: I think a lot more could be saved through energy conservation. It was said yesterday that the increase in the price in energy will first hit the poor, which is a very solid statement. Why not establish a tax on a sliding scale? Each home would have a low tariff for the first so many kilowatts, and then a much higher rate for additional energy, for those who can afford it. This would induce the rich to shut down their electricity about which they do not care today. But if we increase the price of electricity for everybody, we are going to hit the poor people. A sliding scale is a must.

JAMES PARDAU, Assembly Resources and Land Use Committee, California Legislature: Back to the question of onshore facilities. The California Coast Commission is in the final stages of preparing its coastal zone plan for the 1976 legislature. Of course, it is going to be a tough land-use plan, and onshore facilities are probably going to be an element in it. I would like to ask Mr. Hughes whether onshore facilities are required for the kind of OCS drilling the federal government is considering in California, or are there sufficient facilities already in place in California? If the California Coast Commission should deny permits for additional major facilities, what would that mean? Would there be a strong push by the federal government to try to preempt the state in this area?

MR. HUGHES: There are no detailed answers to the question you pose. Certainly there may be a need for additional onshore facilities in California. Whether that need could be taken care of through the expansion of existing facilities or whether new ones would have to be created is not known, nor is it something we can predict today with any degree of certainty, when the actions we are talking about may create pressures five, six, or ten years from now. As to the possibility that the coastal zone plan might either directly or indirectly preclude energy facility siting, I can say that should this become a nationwide phenomenon, it might require that the federal government review whether the national interest is being served when a local area denies energy facility siting. An energy-siting bill has been discussed in the Congress at length over the last five or six years. Whether such a bill will pass during the current session is certainly open to speculation, but we are concerned about those who would say that the federal government ought to wait until everyone's coastal zone plans are completed. There is no obligation for a state to complete a coastal zone plan. States are encouraged to do so under coastal zone legislation, but it takes a long period of time to come up with a plan. We hope, of course, that any such plan will be in place by the time any onshore impact is a reality.

MAYOR BRADLEY: We are going to have to come to an end. We are grateful for the stimulating discussion and for the questions from the audience. We certainly want to thank our panel: Mr. Haynes, Captain Cousteau, Governor Byrne, Secretary Hughes, thank you very much on behalf of AEI's National Energy Project.

LIST OF
CONFERENCE PARTICIPANTS

Bradley, Tom, *Mayor, City of Los Angeles*

Byrne, Brendan, *Governor, State of New Jersey*

Cahill, E. J., *Standard Oil Company of California*

Cahn, Robert, *The Conservation Foundation*

Cousteau, Jacques-Yves, *Eurocean and the Cousteau Society*

Devanney, John, *Professor, Massachusetts Institute of Technology*

Dorfman, Robert, *Professor, Harvard University*

Edmonston, Joseph, *Sierra Club*

Gaskins, Darius, *Department of the Interior*

Hargis, William, *College of William and Mary and University of Virginia*

Haxby, L. P., *Shell Oil Company*

Haynes, H. J., *Standard Oil Company of California*

Heller, Barbara, *Environmental Policy Center*

Hughes, Royston, *Department of the Interior*

Jackson, J. R., Jr., *Exxon Corporation*

Knecht, Robert, *National Oceanic and Atmospheric Administration*

Matthews, Charles, *National Ocean Industries Association*

Mead, Walter, *Professor, University of California, Santa Barbara*

Meeker, Leonard, *Center for Law and Social Policy*

Menard, William, *Professor, Scripps Institution of Oceanography*

Mitchell, Edward J., *American Enterprise Institute and University of Michigan*

Pardau, James, *California Legislature*

Perrine, Richard, *Professor, University of California, Los Angeles*

Radlinski, William, *U.S. Geological Survey*

Reilly, William, *The Conservation Foundation*

Sarguis, Francis, *Get Oil Out, Inc.*

Savit, Carl, *Western Geophysical Company of America*

Snody, Richard, *National Management Association*

Solomon, Robert, *California Energy Conservation Commission*

Tillinghast, Don, *Office of the Attorney General, State of Alaska*

White, Irvin L., *Professor, University of Oklahoma*